Enemy
of Chaos

First Edition

Proudly published in 2009 by
Snowbooks Ltd.
120 Pentonville Road
London
N1 9JN
www.snowbooks.com

ISBN13: 978-1-906727-42-0

A catalogue record for this book is available from the British Library.

An Enemy of Chaos iPhone app is available on iTunes

Read White magazine, Snowbooks' exclusive online magazine

www.whitemagazine.org

Printed and bound in the UK by J F Print Ltd., Sparkford, Somerset

Enemy of Chaos

First Edition

Proudly published in 2009 by
Snowbooks Ltd.
120 Pentonville Road
London
N1 9JN
www.snowbooks.com

ISBN13: 978-1-906727-42-0

A catalogue record for this book is available from the British Library.

An Enemy of Chaos iPhone app is available on iTunes

Read White magazine, Snowbooks' exclusive online magazine

www.whitemagazine.org

Printed and bound in the UK by J F Print Ltd., Sparkford, Somerset

Enemy of Chaos

Leila Johnston

For Grandma, who told me that 'nothing great is ever achieved without enthusiasm' but probably wasn't talking about OCD

HOW TO OVERCOME CHAOS AND TRIUMPH AT YOUR QUEST

You are a highly intelligent ageing geek and your rational mind compensates for your embryonic social skills by a ratio of about 87:13. Although your sense of other people's intentions is limited, you are keen to make a fresh start at your new job. You've been revising your knowledge of science and maths and feel ready to confront the world with your sharpened sword of intellect, hoping the world doesn't come back at you with an actual sword of metal, or a gun. But before you can embark on your modern adventure, you'll need to know three things: your words-per-minute typing speed (WPM), your body mass index (BMI), and your IQ. The bonus number is your OCD score. You don't need to know it for the quest, exactly. You just, like, *need* to know it.

IQ

To work out your IQ, find someone you think is clever and ask them what theirs is. Mentally add 5-10 points to this number and tell yourself the total is your IQ and that you are, statistically, in the 'Top 2%'. There are many tests on the internet but this is the only proper and accurate way to calculate IQ.

BMI

Calculating your BMI is simple. Divide your weight by your height squared. If you don't know your height, you can work it out by multiplying your BMI by your weight. In general, a BMI between 18 and 30 is healthy. Consider celebrating by organising a group package holiday to a Mediterranean resort specially tailored to people with a BMI between 18 and 30.

OCD

To calculate your OCD score, first check you turned the oven off. Check again until you're sure. Add the number of times you've had to check to the number of steps involved in stacking the dishwasher. If the resulting integer is one of the 'bad' ones, turn around three times. Then check the oven again, just in case.

WPM

To calculate your typing speed, divide the number of internet chats you've had in the last week by the time you've spent talking to people in real life ever.

SKILL, STAMINA AND LUCK

To succeed in your mission of fighting chaos through time, you'll rely heavily on skill, stamina and luck.

Roll two dice. Your luck rating corresponds exactly to the total dice score, since dice-rolling is, after all, a measure of luck. In fact, in a sense you could say that all statistics recorded by dice-rolling are ultimately nothing more than records of luck. For this reason, in *Enemy of Chaos*, your stamina score is calculated by rolling the dice 500 times and taking the mean. 'Skill' refers to social skills, so in your case one die should be enough.

CHARACTER SHEET

Name: The 40-year-old Prodigy

Profession: Enemy of Chaos

Aim: To defeat disorder
      wherever it is found

Passport-sized Photo

ENCOUNTERS: EVIL
e.g. Life Insurance Salesman, Madame Tussaud's

ENCOUNTERS: GOOD
e.g. The Undertaker, The Lookmen, The Doctor

ENCOUNTERS: AMBIVALENT
e.g. The Renegade Postman, Demi Moore

II

BMI:
OCD:
WPM:
IQ:

WEAPONS OF ATTACK

e.g. Passive-aggressive notes
Aggressively accurate
Wikipedia editing
'Rubric's Cube' projects order
outwards
Homeopathic tea bag (molecules
contains a memory of tea in
a concentration of 1 part per
10^{400}.)
Anxiety attack etc.

WEAPONS OF DEFENCE
e.g. Life Protection
The compass of Ilkley Moor that always points at things
from the North
Waterproof jacket

INTERNET ACTIVITY

Here's what your laptop browser looks like when you begin your mission.

EMAILS

1 NEW MESSAGE
"Person with superior reasoning ability required for high-flying job. Great future prospects for right candidate. Enthusiasm for irrevocable global catastrophes a must. Please consider the environment before printing this email."

OTHER EMAILS
- The Red Dwarf fan club thank you for your message but regret they're no longer a going concern.
- A company is interested in developing your 'laptop lunchbox' idea, for sneaking your own bento-style meals into cafes without fear of being apprehended.

LIVE CHAT
You have an internet relay chat window open but the only people who ever really private message you are foreigners who think you might be a woman.

OTHER WINDOWS

- An error message where Word has crashed
- A message asking you if you want to update something now or later
- A large, flashing window inviting you to play online casino games and win back all the minutes of your life you've spent closing intrusive pop-ups

INTERNET HISTORY

Definition of Entropy

IMDB page for *Monk*

BBC News article about robot girlfriends

Facebook page of someone you had a crush on 20 years ago

YouTube results for 'teen Asian speed-cuber'

Some obsessive blog by someone who takes photos of their food every day or something

BBC Micro Flash emulator

A Twitter fail window

A MMORPG

A message from a photo hosting site explaining why they're holding half your pictures hostage, and how they'll publish the really embarrassing ones unless you pay them $24 for a 'pro account'

An internet search for 'How long is it acceptable to leave it before giving an unwanted present to a charity shop?'

BOOKMARKS

myfootdoesntbendthatway.com
thisiswhatiimagineyourdadlookslike.com
Ithinkhewantsustofollowhim.org
whoslookingattheeyes.net

idgiveittenminutesifiwereyou.ac.uk
imhavingababyNOW.co.uk
areyousurethisisdecaf.com
imrunningoutofideasforthesenow.org.uk

You look at the job advert again. "Person with superior reasoning ability required." Well that's definitely you, you think, as you switch the lights on and off exactly six times so that your family won't all die in an accident. This job, whatever it is, was made for you. Hoping your new employer will find all your foibles endearing, you head to work, *Aphex Twin* blaring in your ears, the morning sun glinting off your expansive forehead.

THE BRIEFING

You arrive early. There must be some mistake: the address you've been given has led you to a church. You check the address again. 'St Mary's Church'. Seems to be right... A small, sombre-looking man in a black top hat appears from nowhere and scurries up to you.

"I'm very sorry for your loss," he says, doffing the hat obsequiously.

"My loss?"

"Ah. Of course. You don't know yet. Um...pretend I didn't say anything." He fidgets anxiously on the spot.

"Are you an undertaker?" He certainly looks like one. Your eyes wander to the fleet of black estate cars parked outside the church.

"No. I'm a..." He looks around wildly. An ambulance drives past. "Paramedic."

"Are you sure?" You consider his sober attire and proximity to funeral cars. "You really do look like an undertaker."

"Alright, yes. Yes, I am the Undertaker." He smiles apologetically. "Though I suppose you could argue that I'm a kind of paramedic. Anyway come, join us. We're having a little funeral. Just a few friends, you know. Nothing major."

The Undertaker bustles you inside the old church where a small group of dark-clad people are already seated on the front pews. A coffin rests on trestles in the altar, and you note with relief that it's closed. The Undertaker leads you to the front, facing the congregation.

"We're here to say goodbye to the Games Master," he says

confidentially, before pushing you forward with such force you almost trip over the coffin. "Everyone, this is the Enemy of Chaos." He looks at you. "Did you bring any ID?" You show him your passport, open at the photo page. "Ha!" He composes himself. "Do you have anything else? Never mind."* The Undertaker waves a hand over the congregation. "Enemy of Chaos, these are the mourners."

Since they seem to disdain the usual cultural fashion cues, you find the mourners' ages and genders indeterminate. Looking around, you notice a statistically significant sample are wearing T-shirts with computer science jokes on them. They're all dressed in black, and there's a slight tension, almost as though everyone knows they should be chatting, but no one is quite sure how to start a conversation without making eye contact. A disproportionate number occupy extreme ends of the normal body weight spectrum and several are even eating things out of small rustling bags, like they're at the cinema.

The Undertaker quietly explains to you that they're currently non-player characters, paid to look sad, but they will come into their own later. He explains that he and the Fantasy Universe's other characters form a collaboration, an action group assembled in haste following the Games Master's death. They call themselves the Various Imaginary Characters from Time Immemorial. Or VICTIM, for short. And you, says the Undertaker gently, are to be their new leader; their head VICTIM. The biggest VICTIM

---

* At this point you begin to wonder: what kind of employer hires someone after a quick email exchange? Didn't they want to check out your references, to hear about how you were a star student? Didn't they care that you aced Further Maths, Even Further Maths and We're Still Calling This Maths But It's Really More Of A Feeling Now?

ever. There has never been such a big VICTIM as the one you're about to be.

Introductions over, the Undertaker takes his place at the pulpit and pulls an old Mac laptop from nowhere, announcing: "The Games Master requested I read this out to you all before he died. Erm, obviously before."

With great ceremony, he folds open the computer, which wakes up with a weird mooing noise. Despite the brave dusty rays of spring sun leaking through leaded panes, the church is dim, and the screen illuminates the Undertaker's face as he reads.

"The Last Game," he announces, after a moment's clicking around to get on the wireless network and find the email. "As the Games Master, I have opposed disorder and unpredictability more than most. Regulation, routine and structure have always been paramount in my creations, second only to the core doctrine of 'Never split the party, never get invited to a party'. Unfortunately, life's own structures have finally failed me. The poor sales of my 'Collect all The Data' series of adventure books, along with that embarrassing court case, sent me into a decline from which I never fully recovered. But I am blogging this now, from my deathbed, because the battle against disorder must continue to be fought. A younger apprentice – not even necessarily that much younger – a rule-maker of great potential, will rise up and complete my work. I choose the Enemy of Chaos to inherit my mantle. It is time."

You listen as the details of your astonishing assignment unfold. The Fantasy Universe plays out in glorious synchrony, you learn, with myriad adventures and multiple possible fates for the creatures that inhabit it. The paths we carve through life's more fantastical realms occur not purely by chance, but have traditionally been the result of negotiation between the Games Master and Fate. In recent years, however, hard times befell them both. The Games Master grew old and tired and alcoholic, repeatedly leaving a resentful Fate to raise adventures alone in addition to everything else she had to do just to keep things going round here. But Fate is notoriously fickle, particularly her fingers, and without a power-crazed regulator at the helm, imaginary battles quickly descend into fun. As a new generation of youngsters embraced this lawless world, the Games Master's role gradually became redundant. And by the time he died he was little more than a penniless old wizard reduced to a life of regular but heart-breakingly infrequent trick-or-treating work.

The Games Master's story is indeed a sad one, but you can't help but be excited by the mission he's given you from beyond the grave. For it is you who has been selected to take the hand of destiny and witness – even create – adventures and their inevitable conclusions.

"You'll be assisted on your voyages through time and imagination by an amazing machine that is uniquely sensitive to intolerable increases in social, physical or philosophical entropy. It also works as a phone and has a camera on it, but the camera's not that good."

The Undertaker closes the laptop and asks whether there are any questions. A hand shoots up immediately – a woman with long dreadlocks and a beaded choker. Oh wait. No. It's a man. "Why interfere?" he wants to know.

"Nothing in the future can be accidental," the Undertaker

says. "Life is about working out which things influence which other things, how our choices and decisions affect how things pan out. The life of a VICTIM is a game, and the game is all about the endings. Actually, all games are about the endings, aren't they? It's not the winning that counts, it's the getting it over with." He glances at the coffin and it looks like he really means what he's saying.

"The long-term consequences of our present actions are unforeseeable to us," he goes on. "But if we can send a rule-maker forwards – or at least sideways* – to see what could happen, then there's someone 'keeping a finger in the page' for us, so to speak. Someone who can witness events unfolding at Fate's hand and impose the order she capriciously resists. As imaginary characters we are passive." He turns to you.

"Part of your role, Enemy of Chaos, is to keep us in work, to encounter the members of VICTIM, interact with them and help create a structure in a Fantasy Universe that's dissolving into pandemonium in the absence of the GM. Who knows what the future holds? All we can be sure of is that we alone cannot fight the madness against which the Games Master has so effectively defended us thus far. And without a director, we're all over the place. You have to understand: we're a ship without a captain, and you're a captain without a ship." You can see genuine

---

*   He elaborates on this with recourse to some geometric diagrams and folded bits of paper. Time is still relative, he says, and local to the person journeying; but quantum entanglement allows you to affect things in geographically and temporally speculative locations while your physical coordinates are "protected" by a shield of subjective spacetime. You remain strangely unreassured.

desperation in his pale face. "Like Captain Birdseye. There's no purpose anymore. The Fantasy Universe is rapidly losing all pattern and meaning fooo uhhhhh."

The Undertaker appears to be choking on the words that can't seem to form properly in his mouth. He glances around, looking as exasperated as anyone at a funeral has ever looked. Then he pulls a marker pen out of his pocket and writes something down on the back of a Bible. It says:

'It's already happening'. And with considerable effort, effort that finds work for all the muscles in his head and some of those in his neck, he retches, wheezes and splutters out the words:

"Dooooo you un, un, underst- yes yep yellow yet?!"

To say 'no', turn to page 166.
To say you do, turn to page 37.

USE THE ENTROPY PHONE

Satisfied the text has sent, you put the phone away and wait. Bit by bit, the room winks out of existence. Jumbled shapes appear in its place, shapes you can make out as large letters, commas and question marks. You're back in the maze with the role-players. And now, more than ever, you're spoiling for a fight.

Turn to page 201.

RACE TO STANDARD DEVIATION MOUNTAIN

With Hijack, at gunpoint, holding you at gunpoint, you drive to Madame Tussaud's's lair on the outskirts of London. Travelling through the West End you pass cinema advertisements endorsed with quotes like "Maybe worth a go if you win tickets or something! – The Times", "Probably best wait for it to come out on the internet! – The Telegraph" next to proudly displayed 3/5 stars.

You wind through miles of dirty suburbia until eventually the houses subside, giving way to manicured countryside. As you leave the city the road broadens – but so does the farmland, and in spite of all the guns pointing at all the heads, it's a relief to watch the stacked skyline recede into the distance. Expansive fields and woodland bring a sort of calm to the car, and for a long time no one says anything. The silence is broken just once, when you have to slow down for the St Albans bypass festival*, and Tussaud's whispers, "That is the field where I died," gesturing

---

* The St Albans Bypass Festival has been held every spring since the 1959 opening of the former M10 (since renamed the A4, due to a buy-out by a paper company). On 'M10 Day', the section between St Albans and Hemel Hempstead is closed for 24 hours to allow thousands of local residents to gather on the tarmac, sit in their cars and feast on boiled sweets and limp sandwiches in Tupperware boxes before vomiting on the central reservation then cleaning themselves up with Wet Ones. The festivities typically go on until late into the evening when the crowds disperse and agree to never mention this again to another living soul.

out of the window with the barrel of her gun. Her eyes have a faraway look in them, and turning the gun back on Hijack she adds vaguely, "I see it's still a field."

At length, Madame Tussaud's indicates you have arrived, and you park the car and look up through the windscreen, as you shut the engine off. The sun is setting and through the gloom you can make out a massive dark form looming over you. Tussaud's's laboratory appears to be an artificial hill, a mound surrounded by a moat which seems to be channelling away some kind of foul toxic waste, judging by the number of dead animals nearby and the way it glows. And hums.

From the outside the mound cuts an imposing silhouette. It is punctuated by a tumultuous sea of 40-foot concrete spears, which pierce the earth like the spines of an angered puffer fish. The thorns might have been standing for a hundred years or more, but you get the distinct sense that whatever horror they signpost is as dangerous as ever. "Keep away!" they scream. "Nothing of value is buried here." You note with interest that someone has attempted to cheer up some of the spikes around the entrance with twinkling fairy lights and gnomes. A festive sign at the door confirms your location as 'Standard Deviation Mountain'.

Tussaud's strides up and an automatic door in the side of the mountain slides open to reveal a huge cavern under the concrete domed roof. The mountain is completely hollow, and in the centre of the concrete floor, far beneath the arched roof, you can see a triangular pool filled with viscous clear liquid. Lying on their backs in the goo are three humanoids, their feet at each corner of the triangle, heads pointing in towards the centre.

As you tentatively approach, you can see their eyeballs rolling wildly from side to side and their lips mouthing an unbroken stream of silent words.

"What are they?" As usual, you say it out loud without realising.

"These are my pre-cogs." Madame Tussaud's pats one of them on the head. "Gifted psychics with the ability to see the future before it happens. They're savants, you see; quite brilliant in their way, but of course completely retarded in all others." She unwraps a Twix and the pre-cog continues to try to whisper its silent revelations as she stuffs some biscuit in its mouth.

"Hush now," she snaps. The pre-cog looks like it's choking and you wonder if you should do something, but Madame Tussaud's carries on. "Those two know about the future – they can show me things. This one's lost it lately, to be honest. It can only see things that have already happened." She strokes its bald head with her ancient hand. "More of a post-cog, bless him."

On the other side of the pool one of the pre-cogs is getting quite agitated. "I," it seems to be saying, its whispers increasing in volume until it's announcing with some triumph, "I I I I, I AM I AM I AM."

"Oh, not this again," Tussaud's sighs. "Ignore it." And just when you think the pre-cog has slipped back into its whispering reverie it raises its head out of the liquid with considerable effort and bellows:

"I AM MEGATRON!"

It does sound just like him.

"Like I say, they're not 100% reliable," she mumbles apologetically. "They get mixed up with things they've absorbed from popular culture sometimes. For some reason they really love doing the Megatron thing. I don't know why."*

"What happened to them?" The Weatherman takes half a step forward. Tussaud's glares at him through her wire-framed spectacles, and he rocks back again and looks at his shoes.

"They all had a difficult life, that's for sure. They're triplets – born intertext children, a rare non-fatal genetic condition where the gametes make clever reference to each other when inspected side-by-side by a critical theorist. But there was a serious lack of critical theorists in Milton Keynes in the 1960s, and their parents abandoned them on my doorstep when they were just a few weeks old. I did what any mother would do and raised them as my own. My own slaves."

"Why do you need to see the future anyway?" Hijack pipes up.

"Why? Why?! My pre-cogs are able to see crimes before they are committed. Mainly by me. Don't you get it? If you have knowledge of the future – of your own future – you have all the power you need to rule the world!" She looks happily at the pre-cogs and you think you can see tears of emotion in her eyes.

"Ever since I made my first mediocre waxwork I have been obsessed with the idea of people standing incredibly still. I collected dressmakers' dummies, statues, shop mannequins,

---

* Megatron's first words after centuries in cryostasis – "I am Megatron" – remain one of the universe's great mysteries. The Decepticon's waking statement is surprisingly declarative and volunteered in the absence of the expected "Who are you?" question, leading one to wonder whether he is in fact Megatron, or just one of those terrible impressionists who has to say who they are pretending to be otherwise no one will know.

trophies, paraplegics, anything. More than anything, I dreamed of holding a moment; of everything staying just where it was for always. A bead of coffee on the side of a cup, an ice crystal in a wintery leaf – a world stopped perfectly still, the same, forever."

"And that's why you made the terrible wax musuem?" The Weatherman sounds incredulous. "To quench your insatiable thirst for a world that never moves?"

Tussaud's nods. "Yes, that is why." And then, with one eyebrow raised, she throws a piercing look at the three of you in turn. "Why? Does that seem too simple to you?"

If that seems too simple to you, complicate the situation by using the Occam's beard. Turn to page 48.

If not, turn to page 178.

DUNGEONS AND DRAGONS

Eventually you band together with a female crafter who has knitted her own Mario-themed fall-out shelter and a male medieval sex guy who lives in his own 'dungeon'. Both have adjusted extremely comfortably to a world without civilisation and are getting on very well with each other. Possibly a bit too well, you think, eyeing them warily. Packing some mead, the three of you aim for the nearest Tube station. But the lift has been damaged in the blast, and now seems strong enough to take only two people at a time.

You shudder at the thought of these whimsical hobbyists being allowed to accidentally repopulate the earth with detail-obsessed weirdos – if you're not going to, why should they? – and, resolving to keep them apart, take the crafter down first before going back for the medievalist. Leaving him on the platform, you take the girl back up to the surface with you (much to her homely confusion) where you quickly discover that she is in fact a raucous drunk who can't be trusted with alcohol – so back down you go with the mead. Luckily the medievalist is teetotal despite his useful beer-making skills, because he's a straight-edge Wiccan or whatever, so it's safe to leave the homebrew down there while you return for the girl.

Finally, the three of you stand safely on the platform with you in the middle, and that's when it hits you: the creeping sensation that you're not alone. The emergency lighting is mainly inadequate but a little exploration reveals there's a farmer down here too, with his own team of survivors: a fox, a chicken and a bag of grain. The tension is unbearable. You exchange a look with the farmer. The medievalist is checking out the grain. The dungeon guy, worryingly, has his eye on the chicken. With the sinking feeling there's about to be the mother of all fights, you throw yourself onto the tracks, lie face down and wait for London's public transport infrastructure to get going again.

THE END

THE SILENT MAJORITY

Luckily a noise on the other side of the room distracts them. A self-appointed leader zombie who, it appears from his insufferable air of unearned confidence, used to be a man in his twenties, is clinking two mugs together. The room falls silent and waits. The 20-something zombie says simply, "Brains?" and the room sounds its approval with the creatures clapping hands or possibly other body parts where their hands have failed them. He distributes flyers to everyone and, as he sits down again, you look at the piece of paper in your hand.

"HAI I CAN HAZ LOCUTOR? WE NEEDS UR SPEEKS KTHXBY". Next to the words, a phone number, and a picture of a zombie chewing winsomely on a microphone.

Clearly this café chain is the world hub for zombie activity, and this particular branch is the flagship – the original, the biggest, and something of a mecca for the creatures. Wherever meetings need to be held, whenever negotiations need to take place, they happen here. It also dawns on you that you'd be perfect as their 'locutor'; you're one of the only survivors in the area, and your insensitivity to physical appearances means you're pretty unfazed by the zombies' fundamental repulsiveness and vice versa. Which is why you're seriously considering getting the hell out of there – the last thing you need is another job. Or is it?

To volunteer to be Locutus of Zombie, turn to page 110.

To attempt to fight them with whatever you have on you, turn to page 191.

WAKING UP DEAD

You wake up to find you're still asleep. The world is awash with strange images and smells. There are voices, too, swimming in and out of your head, or maybe it's your head swimming in and out of the voices; so hard to tell with this pain. Oh yes, the pain! So much pain. You force your eyes open but the strange thoughts continue: there's a globe with the sky built in. Here's a big green Bermuda Triangle. And there's Doctor Patterson sitting on the bed next to yours taking a massive hit from a bong. He clocks you looking at him. "You're not hallucinating," he says, gently blowing the smoke out of the side of his mouth. "It dulls the pain. Mine, not yours! My God, nothing could –" and stops himself, glancing around quickly in a mock panic.

As your peripheral vision returns you notice the good-looking trainee doctors bent over your bed, their soothing voices forming antiseptic waves that lap around your head and drift in through your ears.

"We gave you some of the patient's blood…" "…You may feel a little different…" "…Er, guys? Are his eyes meant to be that colour?"

Then you feel the hunger. The unbelievable hunger. You try to talk, but it comes out all funny.

"He's putting it on." It's Dr Patterson's voice. You rasp. It's someone else's rasp. Something else's.

"It sounds like he's having trouble breathing."

"Pfft, he's not even trying. You know what they say about breathing," Dr Patterson takes another drag on the bong as if to demonstrate. "Fifty percent inspiration, fifty percent exhalation."

"Shush! I think he's trying to tell us something!" And finally you get it out, what you've been needing to say the whole time. After a brief stammer, obviously.

"B-b-b-b- BRAAAAINNNNNNSSS!" Yes. You know what you need. The doctors don't stand a chance.

"Oh God! No. No? No… NO!"

THE END

SURVIVAL

You notice the Daily Mail has provided an online brochure about surviving the zombie apocalypse. The graphics are similar to the Government's 1980s pamphlet 'PROTECT AND SURVIVE', but the Mail's publication is called 'FEAR AND ANGER'. After reading the leaflet you find you are both outraged at the state of the country and too afraid to act on this fury. You notice you're also shuddering violently: the statistics on cancer, obesity, eggs, teenagers and toothpaste are many times more frightening than the idea of a biblical end time. While before you were concerned and perhaps slightly autistic, now you are a quivering shell of cold terror. The sound of shattering glass very near by makes you jump, but relief floods your body when you realise: this is it. Your time is up. Relief because, in all honesty, after reading about the state of the health service in this country nowadays, a quick painful death followed by reanimation as a flesh-eating corpse will be a blessed release.

THE END

FUTURES OF CHAOS

You hold down the phone's 'on' button with one hand and throw the dice with the other. As they tumble across the ground the machine winks into life and you find yourself squeezing your eyes shut and burying your head in your shoulder because, quite suddenly, there's far too much light in the world. It's an electrifying blaze that seeps through to the very core of you, a light with intent that slowly begins to take on recognisable form. There are very many possible starting points from a dual dice throw, and combined with the Entropy Phone, just as many end points too. The adventures open to you at this point are as varied as they are numerous. So, with the dice still rolling and the phone still tediously bootstrapping, you glimpse hints of futures; splinters of scenarios that might have been triggered had the initial conditions been different. And slowly the fragments gather to form bizarre, disordered vignettes – a kaleidoscopic tableau of a universe without a Games Master.

Still cringing, you watch in closed-eyed amazement as, in one possible future, the virtual and physical realms gradually blend together over time until such a point that only a race of super-fast-loading killer favicons remain. Only then – too late – will mankind realise their fatal error in mindlessly insisting that favicons always load first. Another future universe is ruled from the flamboyant Sex City, a many-spired metropolis floating freely in space. Sex City began as a pornographic website but, due to search engines consistently omitting 'and' and 'the' from typed strings, caught all the web traffic intended for the popular TV show, and eventually became rich enough to reinvent itself as the only pornographic superpower. A third future sees safaris and motorways finally merge together in a well-matched battle of lions versus slow-moving traffic, while in a different far-off time, advances in forensics allow the body buried under the Tomb of the Unknown Soldier monument to be formally identified, effectively erasing the national memory of all those who died in sacrifice. As the Tomb of the Known Soldier can only immortalise the death of one man, he is subsequently resented by all the other soldiers who won't get fancy memorials dedicated to them, and the monument is regularly defaced with obscene graffiti.

At this point, the phone beeps. You have a text message.

"To stop the sequence and begin your adventure, please text 'STOP' to 5559."

Turn to page 202.

SAY YES

"Excellent."

The Undertaker has a sip of water and seems momentarily revived. You feel he's really trying very hard to look dignified and erudite, but has no real idea about the meaning of the words he has been reading.

"Enemy of Chaos," he says. "Your quest will begin very soon. The wait is finally over." You watch his eyes travel anxiously up to the patches of blue beyond the gothic windows and back down again to his wristwatch. "Or at least, this is the end of the first part of the wait. Do you want to take a break? Let's meet back here in twenty minutes."

Turn to page 161.

COFFEE MOURNING

All in all it's not the most relaxing environment, but you're still reeling from the day's events and decide you could really use a boost. Cards on the tables boast "30% of customers prefer us to the other two leading high street coffee shops" so you decide to give it a go. Perhaps you can perk yourself up with a really really strong mug of hot flavoured milk? Even in this post-life world, the counter plays host to the usual confused power-play of coffee shops.

There are three members of decomposing staff, each standing proudly behind a different device and each bidding for your order like City boys on the trading floor. It's impossible to know who you're supposed to talk to.

"I have a coffee machine," one seems to say. "Clearly you should pick me." "Ah! But I have the cakes," her spent neighbour suggests, silently indicating an array of overpriced squares in the glass cabinet with the grace of an insensate amputee. Eventually, just to make it stop, you allow one of them to 'win' and the wheels begin to turn on the excessively involved milk-heating-and-pouring production line. A teenaged zombie points at a the price list, and noting all the Italian coffee names have been altered to read 'BRAINS', you take your cup of brown to a table with a circumference slightly smaller than that of a fifty pence piece. Only then do you notice that what the addled deceased have actually composed for you is an undrinkable cup of cold water with a few coffee beans floating in it along with a bit of ear. You sigh, and sip it anyway with the practiced reluctance of a parent whose children are watching him eat one of their 'delicious fairy cakes'.

One thing's for sure: it's true what they said about the end Times. Terrifying, overwhelming, defined by a callous indifference and sense of futility – there seem to be more of these chain coffee shops around than ever. It's like they're self-replicating. In fact, you wouldn't be surprised if Starbucks was expanding faster than the universe itself, creating its own 'Starbucks Space' that will eventually force apart the very fabric of spacetime in a coffee-based Big Bang, destroying all life as we know it before making you put the fucking milk in yourself. You shudder. If it wasn't for the presence of the decomposing risen dead this place would feel really cold and inhuman. Realising you've been thinking aloud again, you decide to find a seat far away from the expired customers who are all now looking at you expectantly.

Turn to page 31.

YOU LIKE HER MORE

It's fair to say you're not great with women. You always go for the wrong side when there's a cheek kiss. You have very few 'moves', and most of them involve performing close-up magic. There are no trick cards in sight, however, so you consult the trusty Swiss Army Life, which recommends 'feigning illness'. And this is how you find yourself sliding a chair to an unthreatening distance from the time travel agent and swallowing hard, choking back those tears.

"What's your name?"

"Andi?"

"Andi? What a beautiful name. Does it have a question mark at the end?" You try to sound casual. "Hey, so you know how they say it takes a year to get over traumatic news – erm, sorry, I've forgotten your name."

"Andi?"

"Could be. Well, Andi?" – what the hell is that short for, by the way? – "I recently found out I've only got a year to live. Sod's law eh. My doctor thinks I'll be overwhelmed by a sense of meaninglessness and my low self-esteem will lead to my death from falling off a cliff while pretending to fall off a cliff to make some girls laugh. Will you help me deal with it? Andi?" She narrows her eyes then points outside at the swirling post-apocalyptic wastelands.

"I don't know if you realise, Mister, but there has been an atomic bomb." Damn. You had genuinely forgotten. "They say we'll be lucky to survive till Christmas. Which is lucky for me, actually, as I am also dying. I think it's the radiation because I wasn't ill before all this war started but now I can't stop vomming all over the shop. The actual shop."

She's still banging on about her imaginary symptoms when another cataclysmic blast goes off outside, freeing the final few shards of broken glass from the shop window and sending them hurtling like bullets through the room, missing your head by inches.

"Well! I think that's got the rest of the survivors," you quip, as your retinas recover. You gently allow the chair to roll into a bit of her personal space. "Just you and me now…"

Andi?, oblivious to the world-repopulating implications of your raised eyebrow, looks at her monitor and proceeds to offer you a choice of flight operators. She begins with the companies who have harnessed the increased background radiation of recent weeks to make aircraft that work through time as well as space. And she explains that time travel only works in a forwards direction.

"Obviously we can't send people back in time," she says, "because…well, we didn't." As she talks and talks you can't help but find her monotone commitment to the accurate statement of the facts utterly captivating. Not to mention her harsh Estuary accent, on which you compliment her more than once. She hands you a brochure to look through with some possible holiday destinations and automatically reels off the agency's seasonal deals, but your eyes are fixed on her lips and your magazine's upside down.

Andi? is saying something about how it's been harder and harder for the industry lately. The catalysation of daylight saving time – that is, the practice of borrowing an hour of daylight per day from sunnier climes who don't need it so much, like a kind of solar energy Robin Hood – has created a massive global light recession. Some smaller countries are struggling by in complete darkness, she says. For the travel industry, as elsewhere, it seems the nuclear apocalypse couldn't have made things much worse.

"To be honest, times are tough. If it wasn't for the radiation-powered Statistical Accelerator I don't know what we'd have done."

"The what?"

"Basically," she says it as though it's three words, "it's like rolling dice a million million times. But instead of dice, it's decisions of any and every kind. And instead of rolling, it's pressing this button," she lays a finger lightly over her keyboard's 'Enter' key. "You just don't want to hold it down too long; I tried it for two seconds and things were pretty crazy??" You glance at the screen where a wireframe 20-sided die is slowly rotating against a black background.

"Oh Andi?" you sigh or ask, still not really listening to what she's saying. "Take us far away from this terrible place." The intoxicating scent of fake tan overwhelms you, but as you lean in she backs off with a shriek and you fall forward awkwardly, your elbow hitting something on the keyboard and holding it down. For a good ten seconds. There's a high-pitched tone, then nothing.

Turn to page 91.

THE SLOW SUICIDE MOVEMENT

You do your best to ignore the call and commit to the decision to do nothing. Things aren't so bad in mediocre-world. Not great, of course, but that's part of the charm, in your eyes. So you stay at the Samaritans, taking calls from individuals with dangerously high self-worth who wrongly think things will be better for everyone if they could only stay alive. Years pass. You watch as the framework of society begin to slow down and break apart from apathy, and the transport system is where it shows up first. In this middling age it gradually becomes impossible to get anywhere at all. The average speed of traffic in London is considerably slower than a hundred years ago, yet still no one seriously considers giving up their car in favour of a penny farthing.* But could it be because of your failure to act on your future self's advice that the decline of civilisation as we know it has finally come to pass? You update your Facebook status with the question. Perhaps your friends will have a witty response.

Things, vehicles, thought, life…all are now slower and generally worse than they've ever been. The travel once said

---

* Of course, it's all about pride really. It's hard for us, as a race, to accept that the pinnacle of achievement was not the wheel but the mobile platform for Facebook that allows us to stay in constant suffocating contact with all the people who've ever crossed our path, while we wait for our earlier invention, the wheel, to get moving again. One day human toes will evolve into wheels, but first two people with the genetic wheel-toe defect will have to be persuaded to sleep with each other. Or forced to, by pushing them towards each other from opposite ends of some kind of track.

to take up 20 or 30 percent of our lives now accounts for 90, leaving hardly any time to complain about all the wasted time. The Government has even described the situation as 'evil', and they should know. When trains and buses are delayed and cancelled, all kinds of people get frustrated. People who have to get to work to earn money to buy their travelcards to get to work. People who need to catch a bus to catch a train, like characters in a transport-themed rewrite of the old lady who swallowed a fly song. And, most ignored of all, people who had been planning to end their lives that day by throwing themselves in front of a much-loved instance of public transport. Not that anyone can be bothered to get too worked up about it.

Alternate routes must be plotted, whether the destination is Wimbledon or Waterloo or the undercarriage of the 8:09 from Paddington. Because in a mediocre society the one group that no one speaks out for, you've noticed, is the suicidal community. Yet their numbers are on the up, even recruiting mediocre celebrities keen to break free of the shackles tying everyone to an average life and an average death, free from severe glory – or severe pain. "It's our right to die," explains former child star Emma Watson in this week's glossy issue of *Celebrity Deaths and Marriages* magazine. "Everyone has the right to death, wrongful imprisonment and abject terror." Emma's is an extreme case, and the magazine has tried to soften her politics with a glamorous shoot of the actress dressed as the Lady of Shalott, a self-inflicted gunshot wound just visible in her right temple.

The transport crisis is a driving force (except of course not literally) behind the increase in suicidal thoughts, but ironically the same crisis ensures that it's harder than ever for people to fulfil their dream of ending it all under – or rather next to and smeared all over the front of – a fast-moving bus or tube carriage. Where once there were special fast train services that omitted the less popular stations in their eagerness to deliver commuters to their homes, now there are special slow ones that omit the distance between stations altogether, offering only the parts of the journey that involve waiting at the platform with the doors open. The country is grinding to a halt, while hundreds dream of being ground to a pulp.

A kind of hysteria sweeps the country as the unbearable lifeness of being builds up. Tensions become too much for many deeply determined suicidals, and the desperate need to end one's life with a spike of excitement reveals itself as the twisted mother of invention. A few people still attempt to throw themselves in front of vehicles, but the handful of trains that are running are now so overcrowded and travel so slowly it's not unusual to see one squeak gently to a halt full feet before the hopeful suicidal, who then has to climb back out and apologise to the people watching on the platform. On one particularly severe occasion, a despondent man in his 30s was said to have tracked a Tube driver to his home and laid carefully in the path of his vacuum cleaner. Others reject transport completely as a lost cause and, taking inspiration from the terrifying public safety videos of the 70s and 80s, play frisbee near electricity substations and touch light-switches with slightly damp fingers.

But you don't want to die; you've had your glory already by travelling bravely through time and space to study and observe this gradual decay. So, you live out your years in happy mediocrity, stop working at the average age, and find a retirement flat in an ordinary suburb. Neither happy nor unhappy, rich nor poor, you listen to U2, decorate your home with Beryl Cook prints, and find yourself enjoying cornflakes for breakfast and ready salted crisps with lunch.

And the older you grow, the more a haze of glory gathers around memories of your youth. Evenings are lonely and no quantity of phone calls to late-night quiz shows is enough phone calls to late-night quiz shows to fill the gnawing vacancy in your soul. You keep budgies, whose lives light up and blink out in series like a poorly-wired Christmas lights but one day, staring at Joey's hard body in the bottom of the cage, the breath is knocked out of you by a devastating realisation. Yes, they did indeed each have their own lovely personality. But it was the same personality. Everything's the same here, forever. You take one last look at Joey, curled like a tight little fist, and as you tip him into the bin forever, you know there's only one person left in the universe who can understand just how much of an outcast you are.

A time machine brought you here to this mediocre world and perhaps a sort of time machine can get you out. You try to explain to your doctor, but he says not to worry, you're probably developing Alzheimer's. From his description that sounds a little like time travel in itself, so you feel kind of okay about it. He asks if there's anyone you can phone to help, and you tell him yes – yes, you think there probably is – and run out of the surgery with the wind in your hair and your toothless mouth a careless smile because for the first time, you know exactly what you have to do.

The door closes behind you and there's not a second to spare. You decide to build the phone, the only phone in the world that will be able to make a call to the past. You work every hour you can stay awake, your head a frenzy of mental activity. The problem completely consumes your attention, and for every day and night of the coming year it's as though you've been possessed by a compulsive madness. You cover the walls of your small flat with scrawled calculations and see numbers and letters everywhere – in the phonebook, on front doors of houses, even on the backs of cars in strange yellow plates. Then, one morning, you wake up on the floor of your kitchen with what you know in your heart to be the answer to reverse-entropy time travel. You upload it to the App Store, only to find there's already a branded version on there and you have to take it down, but not before you've dialled the number. There's just one ring before he answers.

"It's me," you say. "You."

THE END

DEATH IS COMPLICATED

"A little too simple," you tell her, hastily strapping on the Occam's Beard. "I get the feeling there's more you haven't told us. I still don't fully understand."

"Of course. You wouldn't understand. How could you? You haven't seen the museum yet. Gentlemen, the Cryonic Chamber of Horrors."

As she speaks, a wall slides back to reveal an enormous cavern cut out of the mountain. It descends far down into the earth, and is lined with transparent pods. Each pod is about seven feet tall and contains a humanoid shape. You stand on the edge, and as you very very carefully look down into the blackness you have the impression of the terracotta warriors advancing or commuters queuing for a bus.

"Meet my people." Tussaud's's voice is slightly too close behind you and you almost jump down the hole. "The pre-cogs have seen the future. They tell me I will be surrounded by a wonderful stillness; it can only mean these: my visitors. That is absolutely all it can mean. I literally cannot think of anything else they could mean by that."

"But what is the actual museum?" you say, stepping away from the edge.

"We'll get to that."

"And what do you want from us?"

"Ransom!" exclaims a squeaky voice.

"It had crossed my mind," Tussaud's admits, "to ask for some ransom money. For your little friend."

You turn around to see Hijack staring open-mouthed at one

of the vessels. Sure enough, there's a female in an ill-defined superhero costume inside, on some kind of elaborate life support system. Ransom's mask is covered in newspaper clippings spelling the words: 'juST PAy ThE FuCKing RaNS0m'. You wonder if, in some sense, her whole life had been leading up to this moment.

"A-a-and you abducted all these people?" You do a quick count and estimate there are 10,000 transparent vessels, threaded vertically, one below the other from the summit right down to the dark subterranean heart of Standard Deviation Mountain.

"Isn't it brilliant?" Tussaud's smiles, proudly surveying the thousands of bodies hanging in their glittering caskets. "But I can't take all the credit. Some of them paid to be included. Come on, son. Say hi to your dad." And out of the shadows steps a vaguely familiar-looking life insurance salesman.

"Frozen Assets Insurance," he says, holding out a card. "With you till the day you come back to life." Utterly bewildered, you look from him to the crone and back again, but can't find the words.

"Oh G-G-God," you gasp. "You two? How is this possible? He's younger than me. And you! You're like three hundred!" Tussaud's says quietly, "Two hundred and fifty," as the Life Insurance Guy drapes an arm around her shoulders.

"Good to have you back, son."

"I-I-I don't understand how this could have happened!" you cry. "I mean – legally. Chronologically. Anatomically?!"

"Don't shout at your mother," says Life Insurance Guy sternly, and you feel a surge of adolescent angst.

"I didn't ask to be born!"

"Actually, in a way, you did." Your dad leads you back to the post-cog and pulls its limp form out of the conducting fluid so that the gummy mouth is close to your ear.

"Please, let me out!" it says, in what sounds like your voice – but higher pitched.

"That proves nothing!" you cry. "Or…it proves something I don't understand. Which is just as bad!"

"It proves," says your father, "that you were talking in the womb."

There's a swoosh as another wall slides back, revealing a kind of domestic kitchen area. It's a little old-fashioned and not to your taste but there's something reassuringly familiar about it all. Your parents sit you down at the table and your mum offers you some cake and begins to make you a cup of tea.

"You see, your mummy and I loved each other very much," smiles your biological dad. "So we did what any two people in our position would do –"

Tussaud's hands you your tea. "– and decided to create an unusually intelligent child to continue our evil experiments. I said to your father when we met, 'With my frozen eggs and your covert financial interest in delaying death, we could go places!'" She looks a bit dreamy for a moment, but soon goes on. "So we made you. Our child. A uniquely rational infant who will ride out the wax apocalypse here and one day develop a cryorevival technique that will bring us back to rule a competely tranquil world of noiseless human mannequins."

"Whoa!" you yell. "The wax apocalypse?"

"Standard Deviation Mountain is an artificial volcano," explains your mother. "We have a beautiful reservoir deep in the earth's crust; a reservoir filled with wax. Wax! The most mediocre substance of all! There's enough wax here to destroy all life on earth. When the time is right the volcano will erupt, wax will pour through every water supply, and the planet will be preserved forever in a great…waterproof…jacket!" They laugh, but you feel yourself beginning to hyperventilate. Your mum takes a sip of tea.

"What are we without our dreams, son? You must have dreams!" You open your mouth but no words come out, and after a moment she goes on.

"Well maybe not. But anyway, I have a dream. A dream of transforming the planet into a colossal wax museum of itself. However, it is a dream I can only realise with paying visitors."

"We call them 'guests'," smiles your dad.

"Yes, our guests – these cryopreserved survivors – will be woken up once everything on the planet is transformed. With nothing to do but look at waxy stillness, they will have to pay us every day, just to live here!"

"K-k-kidnapping the entire planet?" you splutter, slightly impressed despite yourself. "It'll never work!" Your dad raises a patronising eyebrow.

"That's what they said about Memory Houses."*

---

* Your dad is referring to a controversial government housing project developed during the recession of the early 21st century. Memory Houses are the buildings memory champions explore in their heads as a mnemonic aid. These masters of recollection make up elaborate surreal stories in buildings they 'walk around' to assist in memorising sequences of cards, numbers etc. Extortionately expensive but entirely imaginary, the sale of several Memory Houses went some way to injecting much-needed capital

"Why?" you wail. "Why me?"

"Why you? But I thought you understood! You aren't like other children," says your dad gently. "When other children fall off the swings or burn themselves making pancakes, it hurts them."

"Dad, I'm forty."

"Yes. As I said, you're different to the other kids. Older. In fact you are considerably older than you think: we had you when we were young. As an embryo you were cryogenically preserved until the time was right."

"What do you mean, 'until the time was right'?"

"Until the pre-cogs foresaw that the age of mediocrity was upon us," your mother chips in. "You have the best of each of us; you've inherited our preservation genes. Look at me: technically, I passed away not far from here in 1850, slain in the Battle of Staples Corner. But luckily your father was there." Your parents look at one another in that way no child should ever have to see their parents looking at each other.

"I had been working on a sealing-wax-based life extension technique," your dad continues. "I saved your mother from the jaws of death just in time. It will keep us going for a long time, but it won't protect us forever."

"Which is why we need cryostasis," says your mum. "We'd like you to work with us, son." She takes a step towards you.

---

into the economy. Developed as an emergency measure when the death of the Games Master threw everything into turmoil, the system successfully raised the average UK house price and generated capital for the world's unemployed Memory men and women without encroaching on land or resources.

"You touched my business card," your dad goes on. "It's covered in a film of highly-developed wax extract that is specially tuned to react with your specific DNA. The chances are you're now going to live forever." He edges closer to you. "But your mother and I...we're mortal. Soon it will be time for us to go into our cryostasis sleep." Your parents exchange meaningful looks.

"Son, the technology to reawaken us has yet to be made. You are the only one capable of doing it. Think about it: you can have a life here. Anything you want. We decorated the spare room and everything."

"What about Ransom?" squeaks Hijack, who you realise is still here.

"You'll get her back when our lad's created the antidote," says your dad, and Hijack looks at you, pleadingly.

"I made your favourite for dinner," Madame Tussaud's adds, with hope in her voice. "And if you don't want to stay, well, that's okay too. You know where the door is."

You look around for the door and realise with rising panic that you can't see one anywhere.

To offer to help research cryo-revival, turn to page 223.
To resist, turn to page 108.

NUCLEAR APOCALYPSE: IT'S NOT THE END OF THE WORLD

You're in some kind of desolate urban area and it feels early. Purple-grey clouds suffocate a jagged landscape of towering concrete. Neon signs hum unconvincingly as they sporadically illuminate alleyways strewn with litter. The road in front of you is clogged with abandoned cars creeping out to the horizon like a great grey centipede and, somewhere in the distance, a dog barks. It sounds a bit like it's saying 'sausages' and you have to laugh.

Everything is covered in a thick layer of dirt, and the relief you feel when it begins to rain disappears as soon as the first drop hits your skin. This isn't rain as you know it, but an oily, filthy wetness. You flinch and, casting around desperately for shelter, notice an open building across the road. It looks very much like it was once a convenience store, a suspicion confirmed by the title of the shop, 'Convenience Store', and a collage of fly posters smother the cracked glass door. Maybe it's the desperate sadness of the scene, maybe it's the hideous, unbreathable air, but something about all this makes you feel very uncomfortable. Whatever happened here, it's clear it wasn't good.

To go in the shop, turn to page 63.

To go back to bed for a bit because no one should be up at this hour, turn to page 217.

THE LIVING ORACLE

Somehow, your fame spreads. You can't imagine how; perhaps they have a dance, like bees. But however they do it, the news of the Living Oracle and his amazing internet café reaches existentially troubled zombies the world over. Some travel hundreds of miles to bring you their questions, generally scrawled on bits of paper, always in that funny red ink; and, keen not to disappoint, you do your best to answer them. You're invaluable to them, a gateway to self-knowledge, the only wise elder on a planet populated by grotesque decaying babies.

They're technically proficient but very literal-minded, and, communicating only through notes, the zombies ask you all kinds of questions about the world. Their thoughts are often quite poetic in their elegant simplicity, for example, "When this online map offers a feature to make the map 'bigger' will I see more or less of the world?", "Is it true that there are no bad fats, only bad people?" and "Why is Transformers considered a robot movie and not an alien one?"

You live happily alongside them for years. They don't bother you unless they have a question, and in turn you resist judging them for their compulsive cannibalism. A couple of the creatures hang out with you in the library at the weekends, and you teach them the Dewey Decimal System. They really go for this but, despite their best intentions, you find they tend to get in the way more than anything. The trouble is that zombies are fundamentally brain-damaged, almost by definition, so they tend to be very forgetful and easily confused, and night after night you find yourself staying up to repeat all the work they did during the day. Still, you grow fond of them, and they often come round to your flat in the evenings to watch *The Shawshank Redemption*, which you all particularly enjoy for Andy Dufresne's ingenious and daring library filing system.*

THE END

---

*   The zombies are big Tim Robbins fans. You spend several enjoyable summer afternoons helping them create a homage to *The Hudsucker Proxy*, *The Hudsucker Typo*, a stylish comedy all about jumping out of widows.

DEALING WITH THE MONARCHY

The slow-moving nobility are easily captured and fitted with explosive necklaces, before being helicoptered to a remote island and released. They are given three days to attempt to kill each other until only one survives, otherwise all the necklaces will be detonated. Coming from aristocratic stock, a few pretend to die of a chill or melancholy before the fighting even begins, but these are swiftly returned to the game and on the third day, following a spectacular brawl involving an Uzi, a stun gun, a bulletproof vest and a sawn-off leg, Britain's bloodthirsty Royal Family successfully wipe each other out. You get the Entropy Phone working again and, texting your story back to VICTIM, are pleased to inform them that you have restored order to the universe thanks to your bravery and the selfless sacrifice you demonstrated by causing a nuclear war that wiped out the majority of the human race before eating food meant for a starving family who you then had killed.

THE END

THE FIRST CALLER

Your first call comes from a gruff-sounding male. He's slurring his words badly and seems to be under the influence of alcohol or drugs. As you talk, it slowly becomes clear that the caller was once an actor. He keeps starting to say things, then stopping and correcting himself in a panic, because his contract exempts him from using certain phrases outside of the movies. Somewhat surprisingly perhaps, the forces of mediocrity have not been kind to his career.

As a much younger man, he says, he starred in a film called *The Neverending Story*. With a title like that one could argue that disappointment was always somewhat inevitable. This was certainly the case for the caller, who wishes to remain anonymous, but is happy to tell you that he played the warrior Atreyu in the movie. His story is not a happy one. Once so full of hope and promise, the young actor found his life cursed by the strange post-modern Germanic fairytale. Within months of the film's release, the young actor's career went into rapid decline.

"*Neverending Story* my arse," he rages. "The story sure ended for me. I wish I could go back and warn that kid, you know what I mean?" You nod, forgetting he can't see you, and he adds, "What about you? What would you tell your younger self?"

"I don't know," you tell him. "That the ability to use an ATM is a much weaker power than you think it's going to be?"

"Somehow," he goes on, ignoring you, "my life became a mirror of that movie. I felt I was sent on a quest to make something of my time on Earth. But rather than a tangible quest issued by the Childlike Empress, mine was the mysterious mission of God." He tells you how he began to experience a series of extraordinary religious experiences – visitations even – all of which took place in a field near his home in remote Croydon.

You ask about the visions.

"Not visions. More than that. The Lord performed to me." He clarifies: "He appeared to me as some kind of a musician. A death metal musician."

And yes, this was definitely God, he says, sensing your scepticism. It seems it took him a few months to gain the Lord's trust, but then the caller, who was still just a normal man at that point and not a religious person, was offered a job as roadie to the Almighty.

"That's when it really turned around for me, the day I realised I had a future doing the Lord's work. The Lord's roadie work." You ask why He couldn't carry His own speakers and he gasps. "He's God! Don't you know anything? He only has one hand, and it's made out of cloud."

The caller explains how he found God's divine mission to be elusive and strange, and involved doing a lot of arbitrary things like getting a cosmetic surgery consultation, asking to stand under a stranger's umbrella or having a go on a guide dog, for no reason he could fathom. "Ours is not to wonder why," he keeps saying as he tells you about the All-knowing's habit of presenting him with a lucky talisman before sending him off on each mission. "I remember I had to carry them wherever I went, and they were to bring me good fortune and protect me on my expeditions." You ask him if he can describe these trinkets.

"Well, there was the enormous tea service," he recalls. "I

remember I wasn't to spill a drop or 'The Kingdom will fall'. Then the house of cards, the blancmange – oh, and the baby whale, that was a tough one. It had to be kept wet while out of the water…"

However bizarre and unfathomable his tormenting deity's instructions were, Atreyu nevertheless felt his life was installed with purpose and was grateful to have direction again. You ask him what he does now and he replies:

"Well I'm still a creative artist," a little defensively you think. "But I do other things too. See, I really feel that God is living through me. Vicariously, you know, on account of his having no physical presence as such. I think He" – you can hear the capital – "sees potential in me that he was never able to fulfill by himself. I know it may sound arrogant –"

"A little," you mutter.

"– but I don't mind Him using me really," he continues. "Any way that I can help is okay by me. I'm just glad He finds some peace by it to be honest."

The caller goes on to explain that he believes God failed in his overambitious goals and settled for mediocrity just like everyone else, and tells you how this resulted in him living out his mysterious divine ambitions through an alcoholic former child star. He reveals how the Lord's stifled creative impulses found expression through his mortal body, beginning with simple plasticine models that were a bit rubbish, but going on to invent a number of elaborate languages and even some countries for them to be native to. With the caller as his conduit the Almighty has been admirably conscientious, going so far as to develop political histories for these imaginary territories.

The Lord created national characteristics, dishes and anthems, a series of racist stereotypes and a competitive missile defense system to keep everyone in check if all the racism, food and singing got out of hand. In that sense, God's attempt at creating a virtual world inside the imagination of an unemployed actor has thus been only variably successful. It is in constant danger of ending with imaginary thermonuclear war, and seems to have become more of a responsibility to the caller than he ever imagined it would be when he took the job. The resulting stress has exacerbated his drink and drug problems and challenged his faith more than once.

"It has been worth it though. The Lord brought out a new creative side I didn't know I had," he says. "With Him working through me, I have become a master model-maker. I can build anything – doll's houses, ships in bottles. Dolls in bottles. Bottled dolls. But my speciality is peep-hole perspective theatres, little models of alternative hallways with tiny cardboard people inside. Apartment-dwellers can attach them to the outside of their front doors to liven up the view. Perhaps you've heard of them."

"That was you?!" You're amazed.

"But yeah I do other things, you know," he manages a laugh. "I'm not weird! Graphic design. Bit of web stuff. You know..." The caller tails off but you press him: finally, this is your turf.

"Okay," he gives in. "Mostly I do the missing people on milk cartons. Customers come to me with their chosen picture and any words they want used in case they go missing one day. And you know, business is booming – a lot of people are going missing at the moment. Someone should look into that." Then he thanks you for the chat and tells you he has to go and take his dog for a walk.

"I'm not a dog," growls an indignant voice in the background, "I'm a dragon."

"Everyone thinks you're a dog," says a distant Atreyu, and hangs up.

Turn to page 118.

GO IN THE SHOP

Sick to your stomach and wobbly, you manage to cross the road and enter the shop. It's dark inside, but you can just make out food lining the shelves. Hastily, sensing that time is of the essence, you begin gathering as many tins and jars as you can carry. You're in the process of thrusting the last four packets of Supernoodles into the southernmost regions of your trousers when a man steps out of the shadows.

"What exactly do you think you're doing?" he says.

"A survivor! Thank God!" You rush to embrace him but he pushes you away, alarmed.

"What do you mean?"

"Haven't you been outside? The purple sky? The desolate soulless urban wasteland? I'm afraid – I'm afraid we might be the only ones left!" You grab his elbow and look at the door. "We must find shelter – quick. There isn't much time." But the man doesn't move, except to gently retrieve his arm. "You've never been to Finsbury Park before, I take it."

Reluctantly, you begin to unload the stolen food from your bulging pockets and put them on the counter. But what happened to the imminent nuclear war? You absentmindedly pick up a paper and straighten the ones left on the shelf to make the display more symmetrical. The shopkeeper mutters something about going online if you want to read, before asking whether you're "going to buy that" as he turns towards the open door.

"T-t-t-trust me," you warn (eventually). "If I'm here, something bad is going to happen. It's just the way it works."

"Yes," the man grumbles. "I can believe that. Now if you'll

excuse me I need to get my sign in before closing time."

You feel a terrible sense of foreboding as he heads for the door and, desperate to stall him, you grab something from the magazine rack. "B-b-but! I want to buy this," and as his eyebrows shoot up you notice you're holding up 'Chicks and Tentacles Monthly'. Only a miracle can save you now, so it is with considerable relief that you notice the nuclear bomb going off outside. A blinding light pounds through the sky in a fit of glaring pulses and, for several terrible, silent moments, everything is bleached deathly white.

Turn to page 182.

BACK AT THE FUNERAL

You all file outside, some non-player pallbearers half-heartedly carrying the coffin on one shoulder while passing round potato-based snacks with their free hands. The group stand quietly in the spring sunshine and you reflect for a moment on the contribution of a great and influential realm-spanning individual. A man who at one time had all the power, who directed the mental adventures of millions through his conduits on earth, but whose time has come to pass. And as they lower him into the grave you feel a new dawn is breaking over the world of games. Not literally – it's clearly getting on for lunchtime – but in a meaningful sense, deep inside yourself. With the only individual capable of creating adventures gone, with nothing certain and the Fantasy Universe heading into disarray, a profound sadness gradually gives way to exhilaration as you realise you will have take on the Games Master's challenge if there's to be any kind of future for the members of VICTIM. But your thoughts are interrupted abruptly by a noise coming from somewhere very near by. It's the punchy chorus to 'Burn Baby Burn' and the red-cheeked Undertaker snatches his mobile out of his pocket and answers it. Then his face blanches.

"It's the Games Master," he tells you. "Don't ask me how he's doing this. He says he'll double your salary if you look in the box." Peering past the 20-sided bouquets and down at the coffin, you consider the offer for a split second before deciding 'what the hell' and carefully lowering yourself into the grave.

"Not that box!" The Undertaker shrieks. "Jesus, man! What do you think this is?"

You're still trying to work out how to climb out again when the Undertaker produces a small hinged container backed in suede and drops to one knee to hand it to you in the pit. Inside you find the most beautiful, glittering, translucent pair of six-sided dice you've ever seen. It looks like they're made of crystal, or perspex or something. You can hardly bear to look at them.

"Do you agree to work for us?" the Undertaker begins. "To defeat chaos wherever you encounter it, to continue the good works of the Games Master, for richer for poorer, in sickness and in health, as long as this bizarre and confusing game may last?"

"I suppose," you say.

Handing you the Entropy Phone, which he must have had in his pocket the whole time, the Undertaker says, "As long as you own this device, your world will intersect with the Fantasy Universe."

He goes on to explain that the dice work in tandem with it and that you'll need them from time to time to assist in decision making in the Fantasy Universe. But first of all, you'll need to use them alongside the Entropy Phone to begin your quest. Each numbered side creates tiny variations, immeasurable ripples of randomness that trigger unknowable sequences of events through time and space.

You look down at the three small objects in your hands. It's hard to believe that these, along with all that crap you bought in the shop, are all you need to visit multiple futures, create order from disorder, and keep the characters of Fantasy in business for at least another hour. But believe you must, because whatever happens now is down to you.

Roll the dice. Nice, aren't they? **Now turn to page 35.**

THE TRAVEL AGENCY

The only other business left open within walkable distance is a travel agent's down the road, which still seems to be up and running – thanks, you can only assume, to the bomb-proof qualities of its ancient analogue computer system. Evidently when the Post Office designed Viewdata they anticipated some kind of mass atomic event.

"Hello!" says the only surviving member of staff, with inexplicable enthusiasm, and by the colour of her skin you deduce she has located some gamma rays. She's wearing a hands-free headset over her straw-like hair and looks like the world's most worrying air traffic controller.

"Is there anywhere left to go on holiday?" you ask. "Somewhere, you know, not too hot, too cold, or too radioactive."

"Places you wouldn't even believe?" Her voice goes up at the ends just like her automated smile.

"Oh," you head for the door. "Don't bother then."

"No, I mean…wait! You – you might believe?"

You swing round and look down your spectacles at the seated woman. "I'm afraid," you tell her, "that you will have to say what you mean."

"We're…not just a travel agency, right?" The smile's gone out but her eyes are burning like fire. "Haven't you seen our adverts? They're all over Teletext?"

You want to explain to her that the rest of the world never appreciated the genius of Viewdata in the same way that travel agencies always have and continue to. You want to tell her the thing that guy said about the internet being a series of tubes. You want to teach her so much about science and progress and the normal colour of healthy Caucasian skin. But the next thing she says stops you in your tracks.

"Since the Games Master left and everything went strange we've changed. We're a time travel agency. Great deal on at the moment too – buy a six day holiday, get the previous six days free?"

You look at the woman again. Suddenly she doesn't seem so unattractive.

Attempt to chat up the time travel agent. Roll one die for yourself and one die for her. If the number you throw is higher than the one she throws, you like her more than she likes you, vice versa for the opposite.

Turn to page 198 if her score is higher.

Turn to page 40 if your score is higher.

THE CUBE OF LAW

The maze problem has a difficulty level of at least nine cubic rubes, and calls for specialist equipment. Luckily you picked up the Rubric's Cube in the shop; a few deft turns and twists later, the puzzle is complete and projecting its order onto the surrounding area like some kind of structure-crazed magic glitterball. You watch as, in a surreal dance, punctuation marks glide into their correct places. Letters begin to materialise in the spaces between commas and full stops, and when there are enough letters, recognisable words like 'danger', 'get', 'the', 'hell' and 'out' can be clearly read. In front of you a 'less than' sign and a couple of hyphens have joined forces to create an arrow. It points to another notice. 'Roll the dice'.

Roll one die. If you score a three or more, turn to page 103. If you roll less than a 3, turn to page 70.

THE PROBLEM OF INFINITE REGRESS

The three of you follow the arrow through some sort of portal of wobbly blackness and emerge in what looks very much like a TV studio.

Three actors are standing on a sound stage in front of a blue screen, surrounded by a few large foam punctuation marks. The group turns to face the three of you as you step out of the shadows. "Oh no," they all exclaim in chorus. "That's not how I imagined it at all!"

"Cut!" The Director leaps out of her chair and bounds over to you. "Could you try to look a bit more convincingly lost please?"

Someone jumps in front of the camera with a clapper board and a voice shouts "Enemy of Chaos: The Problem of Infinite Regress. Take ten thousand sexdecillion." When you look back, the actors have gone and you are standing in their place. Another you and another pair of role-players step out of the shadows just as you did, and you all gasp, "Oh no, that's not how I imagined it at all". You look at the duplicate you, and duplicate you looks at you. For a long time, no one says anything.

"We have got to stop meeting like this," you whisper.

"I've been thinking," the second you replies. "There might be a way out for you."

"I'm listening."

And to the Director's considerable frustration, paradox-you calls a break on the filming and takes you outside to a train station. You follow him onto the first train that arrives.

After a few embarrassing moments where you both lunge for the same seat, then both lunge for the one next to it, you settle down next to each other. Avoiding the bemused expressions of other passengers, paradox-you begins.

"You created me." He looks quite sad, you think, and fine lines web his face in a way you've never noticed on your own, during any of your regular checks for cancerous moles. "I can't make this stop or I'll cease to exist." You look around in a panic.

"Not the train, you idiot. The causality loop."

It sinks in. "I can't believe you tricked me!" Your head is pounding. "Why did you bring me here?"

"To respond to the latter point first," he begins, and you wonder when you started talking like such an arse, "my existence is destined to be short. But however fleeting my time on this earth shall be, its entire purpose is this conversation. Without taking care to ensure everything happens exactly the same way, every time, I'll have no life at all – and some life, however strange and post-modern, is preferable to none at all. Besides, I like a good predictable routine as you know. But enough about me. I brought you here to give you something."

Then something outside catches his eye and he looks out of the window as the train next to yours begins to pull away from the station, creating a strange sensation in your stomach. "It's the waterfall effect," he says, and you remember that his stomach is your stomach, too. "They call it that because your eyes think you're moving and your stomach doesn't. And then you wet yourself."

"Uh-hm sorry," you say, losing patience now. "But weren't

you going to give me something?"

"Oh yes…" And the paradox-you hands over a cellophane-wrapped pack of six DVDs. The word 'Parabox set' is printed on the front over a photoshopped montage of your face looking at your face on a television set. The you on the TV is looking at a you on a smaller TV, who in turn is watching you watching you on a TV inside his TV, and so on forever, with the mesmerising visual effect of a concertina-ed tunnel of tellies and yous disappearing into blackness in the centre of the picture. There's also a sticker declaring it was once involved in a Borders 3-for-2 deal. The alternative you nods approvingly as you try to take it all in. "Parabox set."

You turn the thing over in your hands, examining it with your fingers. It looks like a regular box set, you think. "I know it looks like a regular box set," your double laughs. "But it's not!" He leans in close, and his voice is suddenly anxious. "Promise me, whatever you do, you won't watch it. Not ever. Are we clear?"

You look down at the glossy wrapped object and mutter with all the disappointment of a man who's bought Coke 'with a twist of lemon' by mistake and now has to go through with drinking it or it'll be a waste, even though it'll make him sick.

"This is. Without a doubt. The worst present I've ever had."

According to paradox-you, who has purchased a packet of crisps from the buffet trolley and is eating them noisily in between paradigm-shattering revelations, the key to breaking infinite regress paradoxes is something called the "fixed point". The ongoing existence of the Parabox set constitutes one such fixed point – an "out" that will free you from any time travel paradox. The box set may or may not contain a "finished version"

of the film that was being made when you stepped out of the maze onto the stage. It is thought to consist of a finished record, footage of role-players pretending to be actors pretending to be role-players pretending to be the fantasy characters in the maze at the moment you entered the story. Owning your own box set, your duplicate explains, gives you a powerful defence against involuntary circularity. With paradox safely trapped and packed up in your inventory, you can continue to go about your business in a safe, linear, causal fashion. Just as long as you never watch it. So many questions fill your head. Is this guy more real than you are? What's on these DVDs? When an actor doesn't know he's acting, is it still fiction? What are you meant to do when you smell gas? Is that thing loaded? You stare at the alternate you in disbelief.

"I know it's a lot to take in," he's smiling kindly, but you can barely get the words out.

"Y-y-you mean I'm...an actor?"

"Just don't watch the DVDs. And try to avoid paradoxes." He thrusts the trainline magazine on you and turns away to text someone on his phone.

To read the publication, turn to page 225.

To press your paradox-self about what's really going on here, turn to page 79.

USE THE METAPHORICAL ATTACK DEVICE

Although the group appears essentially innocuous, you are, as ever, overwhelmed by the inexplicable urge to murder, and it's not long before you catch yourself plotting to kill them off one by one. The group resists your attempts at physical assault but it's possible they may yet be susceptible to a more abstract approach, so you initiate the Metaphorical Attack Device. For some minutes nothing happens, but then, before you quite know what's happened, you've befriended Hijack and stabbed him in the back, invaded the Linguist's privacy and jumped down the Weatherman's throat. The Weatherman parries by brewing a storm in a teacup, but you accuse him of making a mountain out of a molehill. Still bleeding on the floor, Hijack instructs the mountain to come to Muhammad, who asks to be left out of this.

You flee with the Lookmen in hot pursuit, but as you walk into a bar the Weatherman is interrogated about his 'long face', the Linguist says "Ouch", and Hijack is turned away by the bouncers who don't believe he's over 18. The metaphorical device must still be working, though, because to your considerable surprise the place turns out to be a Moebius Strip joint. The girls are beautiful if kind of one-dimensional, and the night seems to go on forever.

THE END

KILL THE POSTMAN, STEAL HIS UNIFORM AND ESCAPE

You grab a letter and deftly administer a fatal paper cut to Postman Alan's throat, before quickly stripping him naked. There isn't time to dress his bloodied corpse in your own clothes so you just sort of lay them over him, jump on the bike and pedal away quickly without looking back. Your heart is racing as you flee the crime scene, clouds of dust and a trail of elastic bands in your wake.

There's a map and a boat rental receipt in the postman's pocket. It seems he'd been planning a trip to a remote island in the middle of the North Sea. From a quick internet search you learn the island is a man-made construction built on the wreckage of abandoned oil rigs, completely self-contained with its own government and currency. Employees of the Royal Mail were the only outsiders to visit the island since civilisation was established, making deliveries daily until the company went bust due to the debilitating cost of flying to a remote island every day while keeping stamp prices under the legal cap of 40p.

As a result of this, the simple islanders came to view British postmen as ethereal beings invested with mystical powers, and when they stopped making their rounds, the population was thrown into a panic. The islanders built replica doors out of driftwood and posted crabs and bits of seaweed through the slots every morning without fail as if their commitment to routine alone might persuade the mysterious uniformed gods to bring them their 'deliveries' once again. But no deliveries were forthcoming, and in its desperation their faith developed an overtly superstitious aspect, as the islanders took to believing that if they always used the postcode then maybe, just maybe, everything would be okay and they would see their gifts once more.

The boat Alan had hired turns out to be woefully inadequate for such a long, rough journey and you end up having to throw all your possessions overboard before you get to your destination, both to prevent it from sinking and to stop yourself getting distracted by the internet when you should be rowing.

Unsurprisingly, on arrival, you're instantly revered as the divine answer to their prayers for a 'Second Post', and showered in gifts. You return the favour, handing over the Emergency Universal Present, and the islanders gather and whistle their tuneless postman-whistle national anthem in your honour. Despite their peculiar insular intensities, the inhabitants' lifestyle is pretty laid-back and, after a few months of plotting your escape, you give in to your lot and settle in nicely to your new life as a postman-deity.

THE END

THE EVERYTHING £1 SHOP

As promised in its name, the shop sells everything for £1. With the emphasis on 'everything' and 'a pound'. As you walk around, you can't believe your eyes. Some of the things are nominally portable, such as the zebra crossings that you can roll up and carry around on your back and the discreet hand-warmer powered by an enormous sail you strap to your shoulders. There's a 'things you only find in other people's houses' section with weird drinking glasses and creepy family portraits. There are nets for cut-out-and-build mini suitcases to assemble and place on the conveyor belt in sushi restaurants. You even spot a row of tax discs that double as blue plaques to commemorate the cars that famous people were conceived in. You are limited by a sense you ought to buy something useful, however, so after careful consideration you pick out the following:

- Rubric's Cube: when solved, imposes a convention on surrounding chaos.
- Homeopathic tea-bags: capable of producing millions of cups of tea. The water molecules in each cup made from homeopathic tea contain the memory of refreshment in a concentration of 1 part per 10^{400}.
- The Compass of Ilkley Moor: only points at people from the North.
- A box labelled 'Emergency Universal Present' for those occasions when you're given a gift unexpectedly and have nothing with which to reciprocate.
- A 'Swiss army life', where instead of hoof-picks and

unusable scissors the prongs are inscribed with invaluable tips for surviving any situation.

- A battery charger and a battery charger charger.
- A sachet of fibres labelled 'Occam's Beard' which promises that, when applied to the chin, "The messiest and most convoluted explanation for a phenomenon is most likely the correct explanation."
- A card from 'Frozen Assets Insurance: Laughing in the face of your family's bereavement' that someone must have left on the counter.
- Metaphorical Attack Device: for situations where literal violence isn't the answer.
- Graphic Randomiser: a coin in a small pouch with neither a 'head' nor a 'tail' side.

You head to the till where a youth listening to music on his headphones is buying some tobacco from a man having a conversation with someone else on his phone. They successfully conduct a transaction using universal sign language and you walk up and hand over your £1.

Add the purchased goods to your itinerary and turn to page 65.

ASK ABOUT THE SCIENCE

"Fine," he says. "We all need the science part. The Universe we know is not in its typical state. It's a statistical anomaly, but its era of weirdness is coming to an end. It's the reason the Games Master has handed over to you, and the reason we're here now, talking about this. OK?"

To ask more, turn to page 130.

If you've had enough of your alter-ego now and fancy a little light reading instead, turn to page 225.

USE THE SWISS ARMY LIFE

You pull out a tool at random. It's a sort of emergency metal lolly stick inscribed with the words 'Can't help, sorry. Try the Ilkley Moor Compass'. The compass points at a black Yorkshire terrier whose name is Jack, so you initiate a national financial structure based on the rules of Blackjack. It seems as good a system as any, and you implement it immediately. So it is that, under your jurisdiction, all economic exchanges revolve around the number 21. Renting the film *28 Days Later* means you also have to rent *Se7en* so you can do the subtraction and generate a valuable number 21. Café loyalty cards are amended so that when you buy 20 coffees you get the 21st free. Children buying ice creams learn to ask the man to do them a "78 Flake" and pocket the change. Base 21 is a difficult system to maintain, however, and eventually you are forced to expand the rules to include other Fibonacci numbers.

THE END

WATCH THE BOX SET

Resisting temptation is not your strong point. Having already seen some of the show, not to mention starred in it, your completist impulses won't let you ignore the fact you have the entire universe in your hands. However rubbish it might turn out to be, you absolutely need to know what happens. So you rent a hotel room by the hour, lock the door and take the phone off the hook. After a minute it starts to make the alarming off-hook warning tone, so you put it back on the cradle. Gliding a fingernail under the cellophane, you let the first DVD case in the set fall into your hand. Your fingers shove the disk into the player before your mind has the chance to stop them.

There is only one DVD menu option, 'The Undirected Cut'. It's your voice over a black screen. "Never watch yourself back," actor-you warns, a little preciously.

The show starts with the Undertaker introducing you to some extras in the church. Unable to tear your eyes away from the screen, you watch the whole thing from beginning to end, the next DVD ready in your hand to load the second the last one finishes. True, there's a slightly unexpected bit on one of the disks where the writer tries to tackle the concept of paradox, but you push on and find it was worth it in the long run. On the whole, you have to admit, it's a masterpiece. You're a genius. As the credits roll on the final disk you can't control yourself any longer and jump to your feet to applaud enthusiastically.

But wait! There's an extra scene. You drop back to your seat, mesmerised. It's you, in a hotel room, watching yourself on the DVD. You glance around for cameras, and the you on the screen glances around for cameras too. It really is you – it's... live? There's a knock on the door. You and TV-you look to the side. You both look forward and catch each other's eye. You raise your right hand, TV-you raises his left, swiftly realises his mistake and raises his right instead. You get up and walk over to look through the peephole, and your on-screen double does the same thing.

It's the hotel cleaner but, to your horror, she has your face. Your legs feel like jelly and, as they give way under you, you collapse onto the bed clutching your head and groaning. At length you try changing channels, but it's no good – it's you again. There you are reading the news. Here's you scoring the winning goal, you selling cheap jewellery on QVC, you singing 'Hallelujah' on VH1. You, you, you. You're trapped in a prison of your own creation. The crazed need for order that has held you in its satisfyingly symmetrical vice-like grip for as long as you can remember has somehow been externalised by your determination to watch the whole DVD box set and is now multiplying rapidly outwards, replicating instances of you across the planet, operating according to some kind of complex meta-order system you cannot begin to understand. While you never saw your need for structure as a problem before, the uncontrollable self-replication that appears to be marching unstoppably across the world is causing nothing but madness; in its wake a trail of death, destruction and, ironically, chaos.

To use the Entropy Phone again, turn to page 23.

To stay where you are and see what happens, turn to page 167.

OF COURSE YOU SAVED THE WOMAN

The pair of you escape through a broad gulf in the maze which is getting broader by the second as commas, ampersands, hyphens and brackets of every size and shape abandon their pretence at stillness and zoom over to the casualty for a good look. The path leads to a door, and when you pass through it you find yourselves in the open air. It's daytime and right now everything seems normal, but you sense that could change at any moment.

"I should warn you that my movements are being influenced by a sort of time machine," you tell the woman. "I have no way of knowing just how strange and different things might get. I apologise in advance if we die or whatever." Your hopes that it sounds impressive dwindle somewhat when it becomes apparent you're standing in the forecourt of a roadside petrol station on an overcast afternoon. There's an awkward moment inside, when you buy a paper and she puts a drink down next to it. When the assistant asks: "Is this all together?" you stammer a sort of "N-n-not really, erm, no," and from close behind you, you hear the woman say, "Wow."

Back outside you sit together on the low wall, where you try to make amends by encouraging the woman, who is named Ariel after the fairy in *The Tempest* and the receiver on the roof, to forget about that loser, but she keeps crying for several minutes after his death. You offer an ear that she takes for sympathetic but is really just picking up an undifferentiated stream of whimpering noises, and one thing leads to another. Before you know what's happened you're in an actual relationship.

It starts excitingly, as these things always do, with the getting-to-know-you part. That feeling you can't get enough of one another, that you're aware you're becoming terrible clichés but don't even care, as you chat deep into the night, typing "You hang up!" and "No YOU hang up!" into your respective internet chat windows. For a while you feel you can talk to her about anything: excessive capitalisation on swimming pool signs; why the *Guardian* magazine has the same aspect ratio as a chequebook these days; and at what point people began to realise *The Simpsons* is about Homer and not Bart. And at intervals throughout these chats you send her ASCII hearts made out of less-than signs and number threes, your fingers sometimes slipping so that you love her the M3 by mistake.

You notice yourself noticing things more; it's as though she's everywhere. Midnight car alarms remind you of her voice. The 10 Items Or Less aisle brings to mind her insistence on the correct use of 'fewer'. With everything about Ariel infusing your existence you can't help but try to work her name into conversations, but find you are, on the whole, able to disguise this by deliberately initiating a disproportionate number of conversations about washing powder.

Turn to page 123.

THE REALISATION

When you're completely honest with yourself, you have to admit you don't really want to be in a relationship with Ariel any more. Who knows what cosmic forces have thrown you together; perhaps the Entropy Phone, perhaps fate. Perhaps animal magnetism. Perhaps actual magnetism. Perhaps none of the above. Perhaps all of the above. All you know for sure is that you have very little in common and you're running dangerously low on things to talk about. You're not even that attracted to her in real life, and are continuing to see her only out of a strange sense of duty to the nerdy ageing males of the world.

Clearly something has to be done, and for a long time the thing you decide to do is nothing. After all, it is always possible that if you retreat from her completely and kind of act like a dick towards her, she might dump you first. Two years pass and it's obvious that passive resistance isn't working; she's not going to end it. If anything, the more poorly you treat her, the more Ariel seems to like you. With every forgotten birthday and anniversary your attractiveness redoubles. With every omitted compliment, she desires you more. You want to tell the men of the world that you've finally discovered what women want: to be completely ignored. And since she just won't give up, it's time to try a different tack.

"The thing is," you tell her one day as you lie in bed together, "I'm gay."

"What?!"

"Yeah. I, er…just noticed. When I was in the shower."

"I'll cure you," she says sleepily, and rolls over.

You try everything, but nothing works. You tell her you're in love with '80s long-distance walker Ffyona Campbell and have agreed to accompany her on a charity trek around the world next time her orbit passes your house. Ariel says that's fine, she'll be there handing you drinks. At one point you sleep rough for six months and come home with a full beard to find Ariel waiting in the kitchen, a tray of muffins in her hand. You affect a Russian accent, drape seaweed around your shoulders and claim to have lost all your memories except how to play the piano, but she just promises to wait 'for as long as it takes' for your memory of her love to return. It's infuriating.

There's something else, too. It is embarrassing to bring up and for a while you can't think of any easy way of broaching the topic. The thing is, Ariel is very pale. She is unusually fond of the dark, which might partly explain it, but deep down you know it's more than that. Something about this woman seriously unsettles you and you can't quite put your finger on it. Sometimes when she looks at you… No. You must be imagining it. So what if she's pale? Lots of people you know are pale with dark circles around their eyes. In fact, some of your best friends are pale with dark circles around their eyes. But in your more anxious moments it does bother you that she has an implacably eerie air about her. That she recoils from garlic, daylight and crucifixes, lacks a reflection, sleeps in a coffin, and transforms into a bat to fly off at night to gorge on fresh virgins. Are you just being paranoid? Probably. Love can do crazy things to a guy.

One evening over dinner you pluck up the courage to ask her

about it, and she puts down her steak and looks up at you with those eyes. Those pink eyes.

"I thought you understood," she says, wiping the blood from her chin. "I'm an albino. If I don't draw the curtains then, erm…"

She carries on chewing for quite a long time. She goes to the fridge and comes back with a bottle of ketchup. She asks if you mind if she puts the telly on. Finally, when it's clear you're not going to stop staring at her until you get an answer, she swallows quickly and offers in a limp little voice:

"If I don't draw the curtains then…anti-vivisectionists rush in and try to rescue me?"

"I thought you were going to say your eyes are sensitive to the light," you tell her.

"Ah. Yes. That would've been better."

Ariel claims the garlic thing is down to an allergy, and if you're honest you have something of an aversion to crucifixes yourself. She's shakier on the blood, reflection and coffin stuff though, and in the end you decide it isn't enough. Bearing in mind her penchant for virgins, you reckon it is probably time to end things before she ends them for you.

You've always believed in the tenet 'If you love them, let them go online', which is why you continue to pay Ariel's broadband bill for a full week after sending a very delicate farewell email in which you tell her you're sorry, but it's over. You say you know that she's an immortal and frankly you're not sure you're ready for that kind of commitment yet.

A month has passed since you sent the email and you've

heard nothing from Ariel. Then one day there's a knock at the door. It's her. She looks like she's been crying. But then you remember: she always looks like she's been crying.

"Can I come in?" she says.

To say 'Yes' turn to page 206.
To say 'No' turn to page 99.

READ THE BROCHURE

You let it fall open on a random page.

"Cryonics is like a packed elevator," it begins. "A last-in first-out process. You'd do well to leave it as long as possible before getting on board because the less time you spend frozen, the better chance scientists will have of reviving you. Hence the title of our popular long-term package: 'Snowballs In Hell'."

"It's effectively putting you on standby," the soothing font enthuses. Something of an understatement, you think, considering some of them are just a head. Cryonics, it says, is a continuum and closely related to the pro-life movement. Just as one could argue that life begins nine months before you emerge from the womb, it's dangerous and potentially offensive to human rights to assume it ends after you stop breathing and your heart stops beating, and you're dead. Life and death are just points on an infinite continuum, it says. Madame Tussaud's Cryonics positions itself somewhere between family entertainment and a kind of palliative care system, a means of continuing to look after sick people after everyone else has given up on you because you're 'inconvenient' or 'past it' or have started to seep through the floorboards and into the ceiling of the flat underneath.

You get out your laptop and log on to the 'Madame Tussaud's Cryonics Museum'. The main website is flashy in a cookie-cutter kind of way, with a starry logo and effigies of celebrities looming at you on rotating plinths, as if presenting themselves for your inspection. They are particularly pleased with their

"Deanimated Dame Judi Dench!" and as her autograph graphic twirls past you're interested to note she draws a little heart over the 'i'.

Turn to page 234.

SPOOKY ACTION AT A DISTANCE

You and Andi? are transported to somewhere very close to the end of Earth's natural lifespan, and looking around, you appear to be the only living creatures on a barren, unpopulated planet. All you can see for miles around is red rubble, dust, and – incongruously – Andi?'s entire workstation, which appears to have made the move more or less intact. You note with interest that Viewdata is still working. The time travel agent continues to resist your attempts to mate, but one day as you're chasing her terrified form across the dunes you see something move in the distance. You can't be sure, but you think it's Demi Moore. You immediately give up on Andi?, who is a six at best, and change course to sprint towards the movie star instead. Approaching the actress you find her to be as ageless as ever; it's amazing. Standing in front of her, gently panting, you ask her how she came to be here in this desolate world, and whether she's still doing the pottery. And what Demi has to tell you is quite astonishing.

In that gentle American brogue, the actress explains that she lives here because it's her natural environment; it's where she feels the most at home. Yes, it is indeed a parched planet, but there's more to this place than meets the eye. For millennia, Earth has been flooded, scorched, and pounded by asteroids. The ozone layer departed centuries ago, the ice caps melted, and all the creatures that walked and swam and flew are now returned to dust under the baking sun. The history of organic genesis is an anthology of stories with no one to tell them, because when a destiny is fulfilled it disappears from sight, falling silent to the ears of the present moment.

Everyone else is long dead – but, says Demi firmly, the Earth is far from unpopulated, no sir. She shakes her long black tresses and you can see some plastic surgery scarring behind her ears. The world is busier than ever. It's crawling with electromagnetic memories, imprints of all the lives once lived. She sits you down on a clay pot and calmly explains to you that her extraordinary agelessness is an evolutionary technique, that her whole life has been building up to this moment of mass-haunting, because she, the famous actress Demi Moore, is exclusively attracted to ghosts.

You must look doubtful because she asks you to recall the film *Ghost*, in which she was in love with Patrick Swayze – and we all know what he was.* Then, as your eyes wander across the arid landscape, she begins to tell you about a rubbish thriller called *Half Light* that she starred in, in which she fancied a lighthouse keeper. He too turned out to be nothing but an apparition. When in 1987 she finally settled down and got married, it was to Bruce Willis, star of popular twist flick *The Sixth Sense*. "I don't want to give away the ending," she says, "but he turns out to be a ghost." You're just trying to remember whether you've ever seen Ashton Kutcher pick anything up when Andi? approaches to tells you she's fixed the device and can send you both back

---

* As an interesting aside, many people don't realise the phrase 'making whoopi' can be traced to the influential matchmaking role of Whoopi Goldberg's character in the 1990 supernatural romance.

in time, although she doesn't know how far, and there's only enough residual power in the computer for one attempt. It has to work.

You both place your hands on the keyboard and close your eyes tightly, but when you open them, Andi? has gone. The thought crosses your mind that she'd rather live out her life alone in the desolate wastelands of a scorched, empty, unexpectedly haunted world than spend one more minute with you. But there are more important issues at hand. Because wherever the Statistical Accelerator has sent you, it isn't home.

Turn to page 134.

THE BAD SAMARITANS

The card takes you to the London headquarters of the Samaritans. It's a surprisingly high-security establishment, possibly a former military citadel, and for some minutes you stand outside, looking up at the spiralling barbed wire and wondering how to get in. Just as you're about to give up, someone slips through in front of you, and you read the entry code as they type it: "999HELP".

At first you're taken aback to discover that the Samaritans still exists in this future at all. But so long as people are depressed or falling on hard times, you suppose, they will need impartial and sympathetic ears to talk to – even in a mediocre world there must be moderately sad people like Les Dennis. As you stay and watch them work, though, it becomes clear that this organisation is nothing like the Samaritans of the early 21st century. There's not a gloomy poster of a downcast soul in sight. No promise of a calm listening ear, no lure of a nonjudgmental highly-trained empath on the other end of the line. The Samaritans of the mediocre future is a very different kettle of fish indeed. And it is overwhelmed – deluged even – with calls from individuals utterly certain of their own specialness, but with no one to discuss it with. As you talk to your new compatriots, everything starts to make a kind of crazy sense.

There are two full-time volunteers at the Samaritans of the mediocre future. One is a highly-evolved version of the typical therapeutic questioner, trained to rephrase statements in a way designed to help people to help themselves. The other is a rhetorical statistician, now out of work but once employed to answer the question 'What are the chances?' whenever it came up in conversation. They generally make a good team, with problems only really arising when the statistician asks the therapist for her opinion on the chances. She invariably replies with a reflexive question about the statistician's thoughts on the chances, creating a meta-rhetorical question which the statistician subsequently has to tackle. The ensuing exchange has the potential for infinite deadlock, and great lengths are taken to avoid it.

Someone hands you a laminated card with "<u>Could you be a Samaritan?</u>" printed at the top in triple-underlined rainbow-effect Comic Sans. Beneath are the unnecessarily italicised words: *"Can you listen to the people who call us here without empathy or any real interest in their problems? Can you judge the caller, talk over them, and fail to establish a relationship of trust with them? Can you make people feel that, whatever happens, they are completely and totally alone?"*

It quickly becomes clear that these bad Samaritans are desperate for staff, and before you have time to protest about the use of Comic Sans or anything else, they've offered you a job, beginning straight away.

"Do you think I'm right for this?" you ask them, slightly thrown by the lack of typical employment protocol.

"Do you think you're right for this?" comes the infuriating reply. This goes on for some time until eventually you give up, they show you to your booth, and the phone rings immediately.

To take this call, turn to page 58.

To get a drink of water and pick up the next one, turn to page 118.

FOR THE LOVE OF POST

You agree to go, but for some reason no one is willing to come with you. This is one journey you must go alone.

The Post Master is based in a neutral territory. The address you've been given leads you to a once-attractive but now partially boarded up, white-painted house in the countryside. There is a small mailbox outside. You knock on the boards nailed over the door and wait for a long time. A very long time. There's no answer. Eventually you pull one of the boards off the door and shove it. You can feel a weight of something pushing back and shove harder. Then there's a sort of fluttering crash, and suddenly it swings easily open and you tumble inside.

It's dim inside the house but you can tell you're surrounded by stuff; standing in a sea of it, in fact. You sweep a hand through the mystery substance and realise: it's post. Letters. Looking through some of them in a shaft of sunlight you note they're unopened, and as you wade across to the next room, you find more of the same. This time, though, the stacks of mail are more orderly to the extent that they're taking on recognisable forms – could it be? A sofa? A three-piece suite made entirely of undelivered parcels? The armchair is facing away from you, but even in the darkness, you can tell it isn't empty.

"I've been expecting you." The Post Master's voice is small, reedy and rather camp, and one hand drums frantically on the papery arm of the seat while he talks. You try to get nearer to see his face, but something stops you. It's an outsize coffee table made from undelivered packages, bound tightly with parcel string.

"Oh yeah," comes the voice again. "Sorry about that. It's just that I – well, I love post." There's a tremble in his voice. "I love it…so much. A lot of people collect stamps, but I say: why stop there? Post has always been so precious to me. I'd never have made it as a postman, you know. I can't bear to part with it." He stops drumming and grips the chairs with both bony hands.

"Things have got out of hand, haven't they? My poor children." His voice cracks. "It breaks my heart when they fight. They're so terribly clever, it's such a waste. Postal workers could rule the world if they'd only sort themselves out. And they don't realise, do they? It's the POST that's the first casualty of this conflict. THE POST!" He kicks up some letters from the floor, which scatter down again like confetti.

"What should I do?" you say, very eager to leave.

"I'll tell you what you must do," he says. After an awkward pause where he scoops some post up into his lap and begins stroking it: "Nuke them all."

It occurs to you that the Post Master has grown insane through years of solitude, with no one to talk to but his post so you check:

"Are you sure?"

"Ten years I've been here. No one's visited. Let me tell you, the postman never rings once. You'll find what you need in my mailbox," he says. "Goodbye!"

Back outside, you open the small mailbox and find it contains a note. "Sorry you were out," it says, in large white letters on a red background. The note is dated 2001. Wow, you think. The postman really does never ring once. There's an address to collect your 'Registered signed-for letter'.

To go to the sorting office on the card, turn to page 128.
To call the number written on it, turn to page 126.

SO LONG, SUCKER

"Sorry," you say. "I think it's best not."

You watch Ariel fly off into the night sky, and almost before you've closed the front door for the fourth time, your life begins its downward spiral. She might have been an insane supernatural murderess, but without her around you're a complete mess. You don't leave the house for weeks. You forget to wash, eat, sleep or line up all your tins so they face outwards. Sometimes you even forget to do the washing up in the right order.

Ariel was pretty much your only friend, and now she's gone you become very lonely very quickly. You start hanging out with a crop circle faking group; an entertaining distraction until your new friend Pete accidentally hangs himself during a routine Mandelbrot Set. You see it all happen. One minute he's walking the circumference line, one end of the rope looped around his neck and the other round the pole in the centre in the regular way; the next he's thrashing around in the wheat and making horrible choking noises. You rush to help, but are unable to free him in time and he dies there and then in your arms. He tilts his purple face up to look at you, and you'll never forget Pete's final words,

"Please," he rasps. "Tell my wife this happened during a sex game."

So this is what you do. A verdict of autoerotic asphyxia is passed, and Pete's shameful secret goes with him to the grave.

After Pete's wake, you return to an empty house. And as you sit on your bed with your head in your hands, you have to accept that you have well and truly lost control. You're in real danger of failing your quest and in even more danger of failing to care. The entropy – the terrible decay – that you were warned would come about in the Games Master's absence has indeed arrived, but it is more frightening than you could have imagined. Because it's not about millions being killed by an asteroid, freaky weather or a global epidemic. It's much worse than that: it's about you. A crushing bleakness seizes your soul as you ponder your life's cascade into pathos, and having considered all the options, you do the only thing there is left to do.

You put the telly on. At least the manic woman on Quizmania offering you £2000 to tell her the name of a fish seems slightly more desperate than you. You pick up the phone and get through to the show immediately.

"It's OK," you say. "You can keep the money; I just want to chat."

You ask her: How did it come to this? Will anyone ever truly understand you again? But eventually even the Quizmania girl hangs up on you, and she surely hasn't had a sensible conversation in months.

During a midnight search for household objects with blades, you discover the Entropy Phone languishing in a kitchen drawer. You're still consumed by thoughts of hurting yourself, but feel compelled to at least see if the device still works. So you charge the battery charger, then the battery, frequently glancing over from your knife-sharpening to see if the red light has turned to green.

Finally it does and you put the blade down. 'STOP', you text. Please stop.

Turn to page 23.

EXPLORE ON FOOT

You can't sleep so, pulling on the slippers and dressing gown your parents have thoughtfully provided, you pad back into the dome and enter the cryochamber with considerable trepidation.

It's probably fair to say that it houses the strangest selection of people you've ever seen under one roof. Some of the pods are fancier than others; you suppose these belong to wealthy volunteers unaware of your parents' evil plan. And as you take in the scene, it occurs to you that you're looking at a veritable celebrity Pompeii. Each body is frozen in their characteristic pose, surrounded by their entombed entourage, apparently killed without consent at the point of their employer's death. The bodies of staff are twisted, posthumously, into appropriately sycophantic gestures, but their faces still speak of the horror and betrayal of terrible final moments. Unsurprisingly, Walt Disney lies in permanent repose in the garb of his most famous character Snow White, and seven Disney employees of below-average height apparently gave their lives to complete the macabre vignette. You bow your head in acknowledgment of their sacrifice, and when you look up realise with some alarm that all the Milky Bar kids are here, frozen in their prime and raising fresh questions about the ethics of Nestlé. Richard Dawkins is over there, a crucifix in one hand, a gun in the other.[*]

There are dozens more of these volunteers, perhaps taken in by your dad's charm and the vain belief that money can buy anything. Each pearlescent vessel is engraved with messages and quotes, and you're able to make some of them out in the dim emergency lighting. One inscription reads: "Driver, the 2019 Tube train disaster. Final words: 'Wake me when we get to Whitechapel'". There's a dinner lady preserved in uniform, as is traditional, and one labelled 'Gok Wan' with the ambivalent epitaph 'Gok Wan used to be really fat, then he lost all the weight. Only to discover that wasn't the problem'.

Turn to page 234.

---

[*]   Not all rational minds have gone for this option of course. Alan Turing (who injected an apple with cyanide before eating it, simultaneously killing himself and inventing the Eucalyptus Locket) famously arranged to have his atoms reconstituted as a particularly difficult German teleprinter code. This has since been stamped onto paper tape, and you can still observe a minute's science by watching him pass through the reconstructed Colossus machine at Bletchley Park today.

ZOMBIE APOCALYPSE: IT'S ALL IN THE HEAD

The entropy-reversing power of the Rubric's Cube may have been stronger than you thought. You can't quite put your finger on it, but somehow things don't quite feel right. A door appears in the wall of the maze, and stepping through it you find yourself standing in the foyer of a large metropolitan hospital. A middle-aged male doctor with a walking stick is talking to a woman in a tight skirt. Occasionally he leans on his cane with one hand and pauses to dig in his pocket for a small container. You lose count of the number of pills he rattles down his throat while you watch. After a few minutes, the woman says something about him doing it her way or getting "even more clinic hours" and click-clacks off down the corridor.

With her still very much in earshot, the doctor throws you a look and says "Hookers!" very loudly. The woman disappears through a door marked 'Administrator', which slams shut behind her. You must look startled because he smiles slightly and offers you a hand.

"Hi," You realise his smile is sarcastic and his accent unplaceable. "I'm the doctor."

"Just The Doctor?"

"No." He frowns, confused. "Doctor Patterson."

Patterson leads you into a small clinic room and pulls the door closed behind him. With his back still turned and in a tone that tells you he'd rather be absolutely anywhere else he asks smartly, "What seems to be the problem?"

"O-o-oh I d-don't know." You're thinking fast, speaking slow, as is so often the way. "Social stuff mainly. For example, I can't really look people in the eye when I'm talking to them. When I do it feels like I'm lying or something."

"Is that true?" he asks, suddenly interested. You look at the floor and have to admit that it isn't. You tell him you're concerned about the solipsism of your universe, the self-referential and post-modern facets of your realm-spanning role as defender of the Fantasy Universe, and Patterson asks you to be quiet and look straight ahead.

Fast and bird-like, the doctor shines a light from one eye to the other, occasionally tilting his head or frowning. "Mmm. It could be an originality-delusion disorder. But don't worry, you wouldn't be the first!" Patterson finishes his examination and decides that there's nothing wrong with you other than the usual constellation of neuroses and social phobias that one would expect from someone with your skills and personality, but as he's packing away his stethoscope he seems struck by a thought.

"Would you say you're quite bright?" he asks, "in an analytical sort of way?" You nod very cautiously. "Hm. Hmmmm! I think we could use a guy like you today. Come with me."

Doctor Patterson leads you to his private office, where a group of unusually good-looking medical students are sitting quietly, facing a whiteboard with the words "If Cillit Bang does that to limescale, what the hell's it doing to my insides?" scrawled on it in shaky handwriting. Gesturing you to sit, Patterson wipes the board with his sleeve, muttering "Just a little experiment," before snatching up a marker and squeaking a big question mark out of it. He spins around to look intently at each of the young medics in turn, then stabs at the air with the marker pen as if he's aiming for an imaginary dartboard.

"What. Do. We. Know?" The doctor's gaze settles a large man in an elegant suit and stage-whispers behind the back of his hand, "Apart from that you and Hottie are doing it."

A young doctor begins, "40-something male. Highly intelligent. Feels a bit 'meh'."

"That's enough for me. Do a brain biopsy."

At this point the Administrator strides forcefully in, her chest stopping just inches from the senior doctor. "Feels a bit 'meh'?"

"I'm sorry," Patterson pulls a patronising face. "Don't you understand our big medical words?"

"You can't do a brain biopsy on someone based on no symptoms. I'm sorry. It's my job on the line here. That's the last word on it." Her hands aren't on her hips but they might as well be.

"OK," Patterson sighs. "You win." He turns to the group. "It's lupus. Do a total body irradiation as well."

"Actually there's a new symptom." Everyone looks at the speaker, a junior doctor near the back. "Signs of psychosis –" he tails off as Doctor Patterson writes 'Middle aged. Mental' on the whiteboard, whirls on his heel and raises an eyebrow at the group. "It could be a form of manifest hypochondria…" he says, but writes on the board 'It's all in the head?' before mouthing theatrically, "PATIENTS LIE."

This fires up the group, and the symptoms keep coming. "Vomiting blood," someone says, before clarifying: "Vomiting other people's blood." And as the differential progresses, you learn the team are treating a patient who has a monotone voice, disregard for personal appearance and a compulsive need for routine. With the exception of his insatiable hunger for brain tissue, you think he sounds like a pretty decent guy.

At length, Patterson looks at you. "How rude of me. We have a guest today. Everyone: this is a freelancer whose insider knowledge of middle-aged nerds and analytical powers are going to help us solve this case. Geek: this is my team."

There's a quick-fire exchange of ideas and suggestions, dense with medical terminology and jokes about the sexual politics of the group, neither of which you find easy to follow. Little more than a minute passes before Patterson announces, "Run the test!" – but an unfeasibly glamorous female doctor speaks up.

"You're talking about an incredibly risky brain biopsy – probably conducted by an Australian – followed by intensive radiation treatment. You're frying his bone marrow, and we don't even know what's wrong with him yet. Patterson: I know you're a maverick and yes, that is attractive in its own way, I can't deny it. But if this doesn't work, our patient is certain to die a horrible agonising death." She sounds very serious. "Are you going to let a man die just to prove a point?"

"The patient's killed before, he could kill again," a blond male doctor counters. "We need to consider our own lives, too."

"Shut it," Patterson holds up a hand. "She said I'm attractive."

The girl shakes her head in despair. "I don't know who's more dangerous! The killing-machine patient or the doctors with complete disregard for human life!"

Patterson empties the pill-box into his mouth. "Hottie's right.

We need to try our treatments out on someone else first; this patient's too interesting to kill. What we need is…a test subject. Any volunteers to get infected with whatever Middle Aged Mental's got? Anyone, say, of roughly the same size, age…" His bright eyes rove sarcastically around the room before landing on you. "…Glasses?"

Roll both dice. If your total is 10 or above, you come up with an escape plan. Turn to page 112.

Otherwise turn to page 32.

JUST SAY NO

"I'd rather not," you tell them. "It's just I'm already employed to battle the forces of chaos and –"

"Oh bollocks to that!" Madame Tussaud's exclaims, rather surprisingly. "That Games Master crap was all just a ruse so we could get the dice on you and get you here."

"What the hell?" You look rapidly from one parent to the other and back again and flap your hands a bit.

"It's true," says your father.

"Th-th-there's no Games Master?" You can't believe it.

"Well, there is, but he's not who everyone thought he was," says your mother.

Your father smiles a terrifying smile. "You're looking at him."

"This is MADNESS!"

"I know it's a lot to take in." Your dad touches you again, but you flinch him off. "The one they thought was the Games Master was just my assistant. You've seen *Saw*, right?"

"B-but…" you're trying to work it out. "W-w-what about the dice?" Your fist releases them on the counter with a clack.

"They're not quite what you think they are." Your dad explains patiently. "We've been controlling them from here." He whips a remote control out of his jacket pocket and points it at the dice, which begin to tumble across the table as though tossed by an invisible hand. You stare open-mouthed for a moment before hastily pulling yourself together.

"I won't do it!" You pound your fists on the table. "Never!"

The dice stop abruptly. It's snakes' eyes.

"The fact is," your dad's voice is like treacle as he inches closer still, "you owe it to us to complete our work. We created you, and you know as well as we do that you can never fit in in the normal world. You're the pinnacle of human evolution, my son! Independent. Indestructable. And…intoxicated?"

You faintly notice Madame Tussaud's holding up a bottle of chloroform and your dad's approving nod. Darkness rings your field of vision, and you're vaguely aware of your primitive brain instinctively crying out "Save my work!" as you slide to the floor and lose consciousness.

THE END

THE WORST OF BOTH WORLDS

The zombies welcome you with open arms and torsos. Before you know what's happened they've invited you to be their impartial diplomat and interpreter, a spokesperson for both sides of the life/death threshold (you're not keen on the term 'medium' for obvious reasons). They keep you in quasi-imprisonment in Starbucks, forcing you to work in the manager's office 'out back' between the strictly enforced hours of 9 and 5 in return for untroubled weekends where you're free to go where you like. So it is that you spend your days as a veritable slave to the beasts, translating zombie media into English and English into zombie (their language is based closely on the conventions of lolcats and easily followed even by a non-native) and acting as an arbitrator in conference calls where survivors and zombies try to hammer out agreements and truces that will keep everyone equally unsatisfied.

It's thirsty work, and one lunchtime you go to the counter and order "Tea. Earl Grey," adding, just in case, "Hot," before taking the best seat in the place and picking up a bit of paper someone had left on the table to make room for your mug[*]. Charmingly oblivious to the fact that they might actually represent the biblical apocalypse, the creatures are obsessed with the idea of the 'Secand come-in' and you realise what you're holding is

---

[*]   They've actually given you a mug of hot water and a separate tea bag, sugar and milk. Presumably in case you change your mind about the tea or take it with just water and sugar.

their holy scripture. It doesn't trouble much of one side of A4.

'One day man wil com in yr world drinkin yr tea. Can has secand come-in. He take away pane and sufrin. KTHXBYE'

Your eyes travel from your Earl Grey to the scripture to the reflection of your face in the teaspoon. Hmm. Probably best not to read too much into it. But then it hits you...the tea! That's it! Of course. Deep in your pocket past the fluff, dice, wrappers, fruit sticker albums and train timetables, the Homeopathic Teabag is there, still intact. Better still, it promises to make enough tea for the entire population of the world. The blurb on the box boasts of the 'anti-entropoxidant' properties of its herbal contents, which, it says, help protect against the damaging effects of ageing.

And so you issue homeopathic anti-entropoxidant beverage to the world's walking dead, who are sceptical at first but, on the whole, go for it when they see the amazing rejuvenating effect it has on their friends. Apart from a few who continue to stubbornly insist that being a zombie is not an 'illness' that 'needs to be cured', the people of the Earth gradually revert to their normal state. Those who were dead before all this started crawl back into their graves; those who were barely alive go back to pronouncing the letter H 'haitch'. Order is restored, entropy successfully defeated. You decide to celebrate by blowing your wages down the Arcade.

Turn to page 193.

GOING ONLINE

You tell the doctor you want to help but you need to do some research, and he agrees. Explaining that you can't use hospital computers because of a new draconian house rule that members of the public aren't allowed access to confidential patient files anymore, he points you towards a nearby library which advertises 'Free Internet Computers'.

The library is quiet, even for a library and it's something of a relief to find yourself sitting in front of a computer again, even if it's not one of yours*. The floor beneath your feet is sticky, and the screen in front of you is open on a recently-typed blog post:

> Whats up crew!!11 Sorry i aint blogged 4 awhile, bin a bit bizzy. NOt relly! i'm jus lazee! Well its finely hapnin, da ded is walkin da urth. i always thinked its 1 of them things that happens 2 other people innit? But 1 minnit Im havin a safe day watchin Holyokes, da next teh rents is ded & theres clappin corpses all up in my face, tryin 2 bite on my skull like its a apal. i mean OMG DRED! Can u imagines?! i is bare scared.
>
> Srsly wot is up?!!!!!1 Wen ur ded ur ded isnt it?!!?! But these iznt ded so im not shore how 2 pwn them? Ive tries everythink sept aimin 4 his hed. Wot else 2 trys? Neway, i finded a sick group of blud 2 roll wiv (see

---

* Your desktop machine is quite distinctive, a case-mod of a very similar computer so subtly done that it's undetectable to the naked eye. You smile a small proud smile as you think about this.

pic!). We agrees da best thinks 2 try splittin up. So am hidin in libry, reckn I'll b safe hear 4 abit? Its blats wack man. OMG NOES!!!!! AJKNS C:DKLJBNAHJJHSBJ HSBDJHBAAAAAAAAAAAAAALKJNA M?CCCM,c,,,,,,·········· ···;//////////////

You look at your feet, having just worked out what the stickiness is. Could all this have been caused by you and your device? Did the Rubric's Cube's entropy-reversing powers somehow overload and actually raise the dead? With an involuntary shiver, you note there are no comments on the blog post, perhaps suggesting that there aren't many survivors left. Unless everyone's just gone over to Twitter. It doesn't look good, but there's still a chance you'll be lucky. Maybe these creatures are starting with the Bebo generation and working their way up to higher quality brains. But whatever it means, whatever the situation is outside, one thing's for certain. You must decide quickly: do you have time to check your email?

To go back to the hospital and warn the others, turn to page 188.

To load up your email just in case you've had anything interesting - sod it, you're probably going to die anyway - turn to page 229.

SAVING POSTMAN ALAN

"Dude, that was pretty low," says the role-play guy when you're clear of the mess. "Letting a woman die like that."

"I saved your life!"

"Yes, but at what cost? Jeez man, I'm not sure I want to be around you right now." He shoves a full stop in front of you and walks off, leaving you blinking in the darkness.

"Wait!" You catch up with him. "Don't leave me here! I'm the Enemy of Chaos."

"Hi. I'm the Renegade Postman. Can you sign for this?" He holds out a letter.

"Wha-wa-what's a R-r-renegade Postman?"

"No time to chat. Especially at that speed. Are you going to sign for it or what? I have other deliveries –"

You sign and take the letter. The postman bustles off into the maze and you shout again. He turns around, clearly irritated.

"R-R-R- Reneg- Ren- Mister. Do you know a way out of here?"

"Of course, come on," he says, adding quietly as he turns away, "Call me Alan if it's easier for you."

Turn to page 162.

THE SCIENCE LECTURE

There's a digital face on the screen in CGA colours, and it's really quite poor graphically. The eyes are little more than black oblongs, the mouth a few red pixels. It has a sort of flat-top hairstyle indicating maleness, but other than that its gender is indeterminate. There's a box for text captions underneath, while the eight pixels of the face's bottom lip flash at intervals as if somehow you can dub the text into the image while reading, using only the voice in your head. Some of the text stays up for far too long while other extensive paragraphs flash past frustratingly before you've finished reading them, but on the whole you get the gist of it.

The head outlines a lot of complicated theories about time travel in the Fantasy Universe. From what you can gather, the first law of relativity is that it must be possible to illustrate all aspects of spacetime with rolled up bits of paper or inflating balloons, and you make a mental note to be wary of any mathematical claim that can't be adequately described with a set square and a used toilet roll. The head tells you that Einstein believed spacetime behaved just like a big rubber sheet and, with renewed respect for the man, you wonder how on earth he found that out and whether it has anything to do with the divorce that resulted in him marrying his cousin.

"You might be wondering if you're causing certain chaotic events," the caption reads as the pixel-mouth flashes. "Think of it as a simulation. All possible events will occur eventually anyway; the futures you will visit are simply possible alternatives based on possible start conditions. Although they will feel supremely real, to couch them in terms of 'reality' as we understand it is meaningless. Think of it as going on holiday to a similar country with a different but related history to ours, like Wales." Yes, the head says. Think of these voyages to the end-points of logical causality as a holiday in Wales. And of course, if you already have a holiday booked, then vice versa.

"You are different,"* it goes on. "You have been chosen from millions of applicants for your aptitude for science, openness to fantasy and unusually low readings of normal human emotional intelligence. You may be expected to witness some terrible things, but your uniquely rational brain will be better able to cope with the distress than most."

Endings, it says, are inevitable, but with some consciousness of the sequence of events that lie in our future we will have the power of order on our side. The head seems particularly concerned to turn the tide on time travel convention, specifically the way that time-travellers so often turn out to be malicious: convicts or terrorists carrying bombs, or cyborgs on a mission to prevent a dystopian future that their very visit to the past engenders. Not you, he says. You, Enemy of Chaos, are already proving yourself to be something special. The pasts are logically unchangeable but the future is chaotic; working on the assumption that unlikeliness moves towards likeliness, almost anything can happen.

---

* The truth is you've always known you were different, even as a small child. When everyone else was running around outside, you were at home making the SID chip in your Commodore 64 sing like an angel. The introduction of BBC microcomputers to your school in the '80s was probably the last time you felt truly empowered (and definitely the last time you were intimate with Granny's Garden).

When the science lecture is over, the pixel man offers to tell you a bit more about the Entropy Phone you've been using so well, so far.

To learn more about the device, turn to page 212.
To bail out — what are you, at school? — turn to page 170.

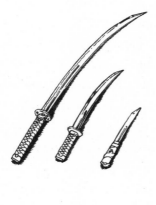

THE BAD SAMARITANS II

The phone rings again and you wait a beat before answering so as not to look too desperate.

"It's me," a familiar voice says. "You."

He certainly sounds like you, but there's a crackle of something in his throat. Illness? Static? Naturally suspicious, you ask why you're calling you here. "The best place to hide a phone call is among other phone calls," he says, and you can't argue with the logic. "It's like bodies," he adds, worryingly. You ask him, "What's my problem?" and "How can I help me?" and he tells you to listen carefully.

"I'm from the future and I need you to do some things, to keep the timelines consistent." Your head immediately crowds with thoughts. Calling people up and telling them you're them and can they run a few chores might work on some people, you think, but not you. But could it really be the future you? What if he's finally come for all that money you borrowed off him as a student? Still, your rational, cautious mind kicks in.

"Why should I believe you? Tell me something only I would know." There's a long pause. Despite the bad line, you think you hear a very faint sigh.

"You live in a basement flat in suburbia," he says, eventually. "In your spare time you're secretly working on designs for the first breath-sensitive computer. You collect the stickers off fruit and keep them in an album because you feel it's wrong to put sticky things in the bin. You tell people you're in your forties but secretly you never stopped counting your age in months. You dislike surprises, socialising and sphenic numbers, so your 30th

birthday was fun. And you have 16 remote controls." It's all true. "Needless to say," he adds drily. "We've had this conversation infinite times already."

"In that case, stop calling me at work!" You hang up and sit breathless for a moment, blinking dumbly at the phone.

Turn to page 169.

THE MAIL WARS

The Occupiers, he tells you, have evolved a heightened sense of indignation to compensate for their incredibly poor eyesight. In thirty years, they have grown into a full-blown society, an inbred civilisation of order-obsessed tunnel-dwellers who have developed from regular blue-collar postmen to perfect delivery machines. They have genetic instincts to sort and deliver, and a love of dressing up in uniforms and collecting information. Outside of society, growing up in near-darkness, and knowing only the conventions of local mail delivery, these creatures learned to communicate largely by lengthy and unnecessarily complex processes such as letter-writing and leaving little cards on each other's doorsteps.

In fact, although the tunnel-dwellers don't have access to broadband, fibre optic phone lines or even electronic switchboards, they have achieved some impressive feats of engineering from humble raw materials: mainly subterranean debris and soil. And as with any war, says Alan the Renegade Postman, technology is the only winner.

You sit for a moment on the edge of someone's garden wishing well, and Alan tells you how the two sides fought savagely for territory. How The Occupiers developed the 'Mail Spray' for fast issue of post to numerous homes at the same time. How The Senders responded with the 'homing stamp', a neat idea intended to take the work out of self-addressed envelopes but nowhere near as cool as the gun. The Occupiers, he says, came back at them with systems to confuse and delay their enemy. Since, by law, all postal workers have to deliver letters in consecutive order, rival posties were easily slowed down by the simple addition of individual digits to the ends of house numbers. The 'addressvelope' was another ingenious invention: an envelope made out of paper printed with an address collage pattern. Unable to determine which is the true address, the postman is forced to deliver the letter to a house at random, behaving contrary to the very essence of his character and earning him ill favour with the true recipient of the letter.

Then Alan stops speaking and points at something in the road. There's a sudden squeaking, scratching sound followed by a metallic clatter and you watch as a ghost-white figure in a postman's uniform slips gracefully out of a manhole. Using all four limbs in a curious half-run, half-gallop, he makes his way over to a parked white van. The creature disappears from view then, after a moment, lopes back to the manhole and dives in, headfirst. The cover glides back over and is still being squeaked tight from underneath when you hear a noise to your right. Alan and you watch in astonishment as, from nowhere, a second – considerably more human – postman rides into view on a bike, parks it up against a tree and disappears behind the same van for a moment. He too emerges in a matter of seconds, before mounting his bike and quickly cycling off the way he came.

A warning finger on his lip, the Renegade Postman leads you onto the suburban battlefield where it becomes clear you have witnessed a typical morning at the mail service: an aggressive scuffle conducted entirely through dirty van graffiti. The language is fairly fruity but, in essence, The Occupiers are threatening to 'return those fuckers to Sender' while their opponents promise that, as far as they're concerned, their enemies are 'Not known at this address'. Alan explains that each side is vying for control of the same territories, and each believes the other to be secretly developing weapons of mass delivery. It is evident to you that an intervention is needed.

"We need your help," the Renegade Postman says. "The Post Master is the only one who can arbitrate but he refuses to sign for anything so we have no way of communicating with him. Someone neutral, someone unthreatening...someone like you needs to talk to him."

To visit the Post Master, turn to page 96.

To give in to a mad urge, turn to page 75.

IF YOU LOVE THEM, LET THEM GO ONLINE

After a few months you decide to throw caution to the wind, grasp the nettle, bite the bullet and just meet up in real life again. On your first date you go to see the sequel to *Groundhog Day*, which is like the first film, with the twist that rather than the same day being lived over and over again, each day is different. For a while, each day feels different to you, too, as you learn things about one another that seem charming and fascinating now but will be obvious and irritating in a couple of years' time. Your heart melts as she tells you about her school nickname, 'Pramface', and how she liked to imagine it referred to her interest in the film *Battleship Potemkin* as the other children pushed her down the stairs. The glasses were a blessing in the end though, as her extremely poor eyesight led to her greatest achievement at the age of just 34: the invention of the 'tag cloud eye test', a much-acclaimed breakthrough that finally provided a use for an aesthetically meaningless fad scourging blogs, while enabling people to perform an essential medical self-assessment without ever needing to rotate their head away from the computer screen. She's a fan of science too, and when she tells you she has a wind turbine on her roof it seems unimaginably cool to you, even when she reveals it's mainly used to power a small decorative windmill in her front room.

After a few weeks of seeing each other regularly, you realise to your interest and mild disgust that she looks almost exactly like you. It's an interesting development for sure, but one that does throw you into a slight panic. Does being attracted to people who look like you mean that you're attracted to your own family, and by extension, yourself? The disturbing conclusion to this line of thinking is that everyone looks basically like everyone else. Which does at least provide one explanation for the difficulty you have telling between faces. You engage in some considerable internal debate about the ethics of the matter, before deciding to stick it out. There are obvious financial advantages to being in a relationship with someone who lets you borrow their photo IDs for entry to a number of libraries, transport systems and sports clubs. You'd be a fool to throw all that away.

After a romantic evening stroll around the London Criminals' Garden*, you end up at her place. She tells you to make yourself at home, and as you remove the last picture from the wall she says, "The OCD thing is interesting." You top up her glass of Tesco's second cheapest red wine so that it's exactly level with yours, and ask what gave it away.

She says not to worry – she finds this very endearing, all your

---

* The London Criminals' Garden was designed and planted by benevolent highwaymen in the 17th century, and is still traditionally maintained after dark by uncaught offenders who want to give something back without turning themselves in. It is located in the middle of a crime hotspot in London's King's Cross, and while its decorative features are certainly a large part of the appeal (the topiaried handcuffs are a particular favourite), more interesting is its unique situation. The garden is a kind of reverse panopticon, a space for safely observing the justice system while remaining invisible to it. On a clear day it is possible to see no less than six sleeping security guards, 25 CCTV cameras, 16 fire escapes and 35 key-concealing flower-pots.

foibles. You leave the room briefly to check the front door is still locked, and on returning find your girlfriend is standing in front of you. It's like looking in a mirror. Realising, after a minute or two, that you are in fact looking in a mirror, you turn to her still seated on the sofa, and take a deep breath.

Turn to page 85.

PATIENCE IS A VIRTUE

You ring the number, which is still active, but doesn't get through to the sorting office.

"Sorry, who am I talking to?" It's the voice of a bored woman at home.

"I-i-it's Mr E. Chaos."

"Patience."

You wait.

"Patience," she says again. "It's my fucking name."

"Sorry, yes. Thought you said, you know, patience."

"Yes, that's what I did say," she says, "Patience." You think she sounds incredibly weary for someone with that name.

"There may be a package for me there? From 2001?"

"Oh my gosh! I never thought —" And the woman explains that the sorting office closed down years ago and was converted into flats. She inherited the phone number and one undelivered package – addressed to a Mr E. O. Chaos. "You're welcome to come and get it," says Patience. "I'd be glad to get rid of it, noisy old bugger."

"Excuse me?"

"Not you," she laughs. "The package. It's kind of…ticking. I think it might be a clock."

So it is through clenched teeth that you hear yourself saying the word "Actually," in a slightly-too-high voice, followed by the words: "Would you mind opening it?"

There is a rustle and a crackle of a receiver against clothing. Her voice again.

"I was right! It's a scales clock."

"A what?"

"A scales clock. Haven't you seen them? When you get to 12 stone it resets you to 1. They are," she says, "brilliant."

"Is there anything else in there?"

The deafening bang that follows very nearly blows the phone out of your hand. Then it's just the dial tone.

Your immense relief at finally diverting a disaster to someone else is short-lived. Browsing the internet the next day, you find reports of an explosion in north London. The apartment block that was once the Post Office Research Station is now the big rubble-filled crater that was once the apartment block. Things could get nasty.

You return to wherever it is that you're sleeping, and find the Entropy Phone is having one of its disconcerting blackouts, a blackout that even holding down the top button and the round button on the front at the same time doesn't seem to fix. You clear your mind of negative thoughts and try to get some sleep. But when you wake up and go out for some milk, everything seems different.

If you have **Life Protection**, turn to page 54.

If you think it's time to phone the number on the **Frozen Assets** card, turn to page 181.

THE SORTING OFFICE
TREASURE HUNT

At the sorting office you find yourself face to face with a sullen young postman who, something tells you, never planned on doing this for a living. He pushes the chef's hat back from his eyes, reads the card and exchanges it for an envelope, which you tear open immediately.

"Sorry you were out," it says, in large white letters on a red background. There's the address of another sorting office, and instructions to pick up your registered letter after '12 minutes'. Since the second sorting office is a good half hour's drive away you get there much too late and are greeted by the news that, yes, they know that's what the card says but they mean 'after' in the sense of 'within' 12 minutes. You protest, but they say they can't help, it's already been returned, and hand you another 'Sorry you were out' card with the address of the first sorting office on it before pulling the shutters down and hanging a sign that reads 'Closed for lunch'.

This goes on for some weeks, the time periods always impossibly short, and the cards 'posting' you backwards and forwards between the two sorting offices, each place exchanging your card for another that must be picked up after five minutes or two minutes or, on one occasion, thirteen seconds. It occurs to you that whatever was supposed to be delivered is being repeatedly abducted by opposing postal workers determined to commandeer the business for themselves. As soon as the letter is about to be put on a delivery van, enemy postal workers seize it, switch it for a card and return the item to their sorting office, where their opponents swap it for a card diverting it to their own sorting office before attempting to thwart their enemies by delivering it themselves, and so on.

One day you collect a notice with the almost impossible pick-up delay of 'four picoseconds' and find yourself rooted to the spot, your amazed eyes shuttling from the card to the woman behind the counter and back again.

"W-w-what the hell?" you stutter. "What am I supposed to do with this?"

The woman looks at you for a moment and blinks a couple of times, then pulls the shutter down and hangs a closed sign.

THE END

STILL NEED MORE SCIENCE

"Tell me more," you say.

"Right. The usual state of the Fantasy Universe is most likely to be one of high entropy, a big mixed-up mess of unpatterned stuff. In those very rare epochs when entropy is low, we get the impression of order. It feels like things are falling into line; we imagine there's a cause followed by an effect. Statistics suggest that we're moving out of that phase now, heading away from a rare point in history where an impression of order is high, back into the disorder that preceded it. The reason time seems to have an ordered past and a chaotic future to you is not just because you are a neurotic nerd with planning issues, but also because one measure of time is entropy, and as we move from low entropy to high entropy, what we look 'back' on always has the impression of order. Remember that chaos is not so far from order really. If it helps, you can imagine the entropy of gas as two sets of marbles moving between adjacent boxes.*"

"Is this happening because the Games Master died?" you ask. "This increasing entropy?"

"It may well be. His influence over the Fantasy Universe was pretty comprehensive and certainly his depression wasn't good

---

*   Here your double refers to research by American mathematician Josiah Gibbs, who discovered the similarities between gas molecules and marbles quite by accident during his controversial study of the effects of chloroform in school playgrounds.

for any of the Imaginary Characters or the space we inhabit. He was troubled for a long time, and he created fewer stories every year; things have been tough for us. But ultimately, he was just a guy. Your –" he corrects himself, "– our brain is the key to recovery. It's so regularly arranged that our consciousness is basically immune to the unchartered waters of increasing entropy that we're heading into. In fact, VICTIM legend has it that the Games Master's final words were –" He stops. "No. No, better not."

"Hey!"

"Alright." A deep breath. "The Games Master's final words were: 'If the Enemy of Chaos can just harness his inner powers to impress order upon the world without being too mental about it, then we might be able to recover meaning for the lives of characters whose existence hinges on the future of structured imaginative play.' He was talking about regular VICTIMs like me."

You frown. "He said that?" Paradox-you nods. "He said that," you try again, "about not being too mental?"

"I don't envy you," he goes on. "The weight of the world, of all the worlds, really is on your shoulders. It may sometimes feel like you are not directly responsible for all possible futures of mankind, its survivals and its destructions, but when times are bad it's important to realise it kind of is all your fault. You might experience the happy endings as personal triumphs, but you can't believe that without also accepting that the devastating apocalypses are very much down to you, too – even if it's not clear exactly how at the point of your arrival on the scene. They still will be."

You can't believe what you're hearing. "Apocalypses?! No one told me about this when I signed up! How can I stop the apocalypses? Apocalypses! Why can't I resist these catastrophes? I feel bad enough when I'm using my browser and a page expires! I don't want the annihilation of the entire universe on my conscience!"

"Usually, there won't be much you can do about it," says your other, gently opening a tube of Pringles. "Best try not to take a galactic apocalypse or mass species extinction too much to heart. Besides, depending on which theory you subscribe to, time is cyclical and relative, so in a sense you've always already been responsible for the destruction of the universe many, many times and it'd seem a bit churlish to get a conscience about it now*." Paradox-you coughs but it sounds quite a lot like a small laugh, and when he begins speaking again, one hand is still cupping his mouth.

"The possibility of eternal recurrence is something you should try to avoid thinking about too much, but like death it's an inescapable phenomenon present everywhere once you start looking for it. It's quite visible even from your current spacetime coordinates, for example in the infinite loop of *Friends* repeats

---

* The question of whether we're traveling through time, or space, or both, is addressed in <u>The Tao of Lost</u>, an ambitious attempt to derive philosophical meaning from the interminable science fiction series of the early 21st century. With reference to an episode entitled 'The one where they all hack through the jungle for 45 minutes' the author writes: "If a tree falls in the forest, does it really fall? And if you travel through time in an environment that is basically unchanged for millions of years so there's no point of reference, does it justify that fifth series?"

on E4, or the recurring 'o' in the middle of Zooey Deschanel's name."

Turn to page 156.

THE FUTURE'S DIM, THE FUTURE'S AVERAGE

It's a cold bright day in April and the clocks are striking thirteen. They're 24-hour clocks; it is lunchtime. As you explore the urban environment in search of a decent sandwich, it gradually becomes clear that you've found a future that has risen phoenix-like from the ashes of global nuclear catastrophe, recovered from devastating environmental and political turmoil, and learned absolutely nothing. It's true, there is no more war or mass genocide – in fact there's nothing exciting at all. Everything's turned out alright, and only alright. After five minutes in this banal world you find yourself craving the threat of impending catastrophe.

The statistical accelerator brought you here, to a future worn down by chance, and its name give a clue to what has happened. Over time, extremes get eroded away. With enough rolls of the dice, a roughly even distribution of numbers always results. And just as time encourages an evening out of dice-scores, so it eventually hosts a general distribution of all other scores. The early 21st-century present that you know so well, directed so strongly towards scoring and assessment, has developed into a future where it's impossible to excel or to fail spectacularly. Nothing's great, but hey! At least everything is fine.

Here the only class you can be is 'middle', the most desirable human height is 'average', and the only place left to live is the Midlands. Biscuit tins overflow with Rich Tea and those ones shaped like little loaves of bread while, for the first time in human history, there is no shortage of schoolteachers. Driving now takes place exclusively down the middle of the road, sports matches can end only when a draw is achieved and Punt and Dennis are back on the telly.

Unsurprisingly, with the principle of mediocrity presiding over all other qualitative systems, culture has become uncompromisingly broad, popular in the least spectacular way[*]. All films are rated 5/10 on the IMDb while online videos and books on Amazon have finally levelled out at a stable two and a half stars. Previously groundbreaking subcultures are now fully integrated into the mainstream, which is also the only stream. Here, no one need worry any more than a moderate amount: being placed squarely in the middle is so inescapably certain that there is simply no incentive to try to do better or fret about not being good enough. Comparison is meaningless: the centre is the only location left – there's just nowhere else to go.

So it is that you arrive at a point in history where events have been so thoroughly randomised they've completed a full lap and become predictable again; a future so ordinary you have no hope of either fitting in or standing out. And as clouds gather in the heavy expanse of mid-grey British sky, it's unclear what difference you can possibly make to a world with no concept of difference.

To use something from your inventory turn to page 172., otherwise turn to page 154.

---

[*]   The Hubble Deep Field, a long exposure of thousands of galaxies, is often considered the best pictorial representation of the 'Principle of Mediocrity', but any student of the subject will tell you that in 1992 the title was gracefully conceded to *The Singing Butler* by Jack Vettriano.

TALK TO THEM

"What is this place?" you ask.

"It'll cost you," comes the reply, almost before you've finished asking the question.

"I don't have any money," you plead.

"Well, do you have the password?" the woman asks.

"Is it 'SysAdmin'?"

"I told you we should've changed that," the man hisses.

And with the knowledge bank unlocked, they talk to you. You learn they are colleagues on a work bonding event, and the part they've been asked to role-play is the part of the argumentative role-player. "To put it simply, we're on a role-play exchange," the woman tells you. "We're role-playing role-players. And somewhere up there, there's a dwarf dressed as me, working in an office." Now it's your turn to laugh, but they don't even smile. "No," says the man. "Really."

They tell you they were promised a safe, supportive environment for their gaming; a great playground for grown-ups paid for by the British taxpayer without their knowledge. But somehow in this post-Games Master universe, the magnetic 3D Maze became mixed up with the giant travel Scrabble, and now they – and you – are trapped in an underground labyrinth of mobile punctuation.

If a certain encrypted order once existed, it doesn't any more; the maze has long since lost its sense of purpose and any motivation to supply a solution. Reduced to a jumble of meaningless markers, it can function only by working its way around whatever's inside it. And as they tell you all this, your eyes fix on the shapes. You notice for the first time that some of the giant characters are not stationary at all. They're shifting slightly – very slightly – on the fringes of your field of vision. They are actually choosing to move, whenever they think you can't see quite see them. In fact, you have such an unsettling impression of punctuation sneaking up on you that you try to silently communicate a warning to the role-players, using facial expressions alone. But your special gurning efforts are just drops in an ocean of regular tics and twitches to the untrained eye, and the role-players continue unfazed.

With nothing to be punctuated by it, they explain, the maze is not a puzzle or a trap but simply random, meaningless form. In a normal maze the form is immobile and it's you who has to create a path of meaning. But in this one – and they deliver this part with very wide eyes – it's the maze which must generate a course around you. You're filled with a curious mixture of relief and alarm as the truth dawns on you: it's not you that's lost, it's the maze.

To use the Rubric's Cube, turn to page 69.

If you think it's time to fight them, turn to page 201.

WHO LOOKS AT THE LOOKMEN?

You call the number, but it's an answering machine message: "We'll be performing in St James's Park this afternoon." You look at the clock on your phone. 10.30am – there is time to kill. Finding a quiet café, you pull out your laptop to record some of your thoughts in a private blog visible only to users of the internet.

"This future appears to be locked into a battle for unusualness," you type, and for a second you think you can feel the boundaries of unusualness move as you write, but it's probably just the coffee. "Goalposts are continually being swiped up, tucked underarm and relocated without warning. The moment any place, ideology or person becomes too similar to another one, the concept of difference slips out of our grasp. And the more elusive it is, the more desirable it becomes."

"Don't you believe it," says a voice. You turn around and see an elderly lady sitting next to you, peering up from her newspaper though thick bifocals. Your hands instinctively pull the laptop closed.

"It's like the diamond industry," the woman says, returning to her paper. She gets out a pen and begins to tackle the crossword. A moment passes and you decide you can't let it go.

"Sorry," you say, faintly annoyed. "In what sense is it like the diamond industry?"

"Artificial scarcity," comes the reply. "Differentness exists, no doubt about that. But there's a lot of folk nowadays whose business depends on it not existing, if you get my drift. There's them that make a good livelihood selling a promise of difference. I suppose folk always need to dream. Things aren't what they were, that's for sure. It's a long time now since we lost the Games Master but nothing's improved. What goes around comes around. Better the devil you know. A stitch in time saves nine. What can you do?"

"I don't know." And you really don't. The old woman sighs, and, passing her newspaper to you across the table, says, "It was a rhetorical question."

The headline on the front page reads "PUBLIC ENEMY NUMBER ONE: METROPOLITAN POLICE FAIL TO CATCH VIGILANTE LOOKMEN" and, underneath an article entitled "WHO LOOKS AT THE LOOKMEN?", there's a photo of a masked man which looks like it came from a CCTV camera. According to the caption, the Lookmen are a group who consider themselves to be 'above the law' but at the same time 'beneath contempt'.

"What does this mean? What does this mean?!" you cry, waving the paper in the crone's face. But her eyes seem far away as she whispers,

"Victim." As you get up to leave she looks back down at the paper and mutters,

"Living sacrifice. Six letters."

You arrive at the event and, finding a crowd gathering, push your way to the front. Three people wearing strange and confusing clothing are standing in a row. They all have ill-defined superhero masks on, and are standing in order of height. You immediately recognise the tallest from the photo in the newspaper, and the smallest dives to the front.

"Ladies and gentlemen, we are The Lookmen. Thank you, thank you." There's a faint smattering of applause.

"I give you: the Weatherman!" He scampers back to his place.

The Weatherman is the tallest by at least a foot and the black umbrella he's holding above his head makes him seem taller and bleaker still. He's wiry and sad-looking even through the mask, with a shabby suit and a faint whiff of addiction clinics about him. There is, you suppose, not much need for meteorologists in this climate – the weather, like everything else, is always the same. But as you ponder his likely unemployment, the Weatherman raises his free hand to the skies and throws his head back with startling drama. There's a clap of thunder, or a lorry in the distance. Hard to say. Then it happens: a few drops of rain begin falling. Barely even rain, really, more that irritating springtime drizzle that gets in your eyes and ruins your newspaper. The crowd tuts and disperses and you wonder whether this may in fact be the worst street theatre you've ever seen. Consummate professionals that they are, the troupe seem determined to continue the show to its bitter end, even if it means performing only to you. As indeed it does. The little one goes on to introduce the others.

"This is Ransom," he says, and you realise for the first time that one of them is female. "She's a master of disguise and the most anonymous of us all. Once Ransom ran a marathon disguised as a finishing line and kept everyone behind her for 26 miles! In fact, she's so anonymous that she'll only speak in radio clips and write in newspaper cuttings! Can you imagine? Takes ages!" You laugh loudly even though it's not very funny because you're the only one left watching and, in fairness to him, he is putting his all into it. Ransom does a sarcastic curtsey, and the small man introduces himself as Hijack.

As you watch, the troupe begins a series of pranks and vignettes, ranging from the amusingly subversive to the outright dangerous. The Weatherman seems to have some means of controlling the elements in a limited way. It's quite a windy day so his claims to create mini-tornadoes are difficult to judge, but he does manage, with a deft flick of the wrist, to freeze a couple having an energetic argument on a nearby bench. Ice encases them in a perpetual anguish, and their lips and fingertips steadily turn the colour of the bluebells at their feet. In fact just seconds pass before the Weatherman thaws them out with another flourish, but as they emerge from their glacial stupor it's clear something fundamental has changed in the relationship.

Oblivious to their dripping wet clothing, the couple suddenly embrace enthusiastically. You hear them express confusion about their dampness and the woman sploshes over to the Weatherman to thank him for saving their relationship. He lights a cigarette for her using only his finger and is just agreeing it's a filthy habit when the woman's former lover, who has been watching the whole thing from the bench, bounds up to the Weatherman. The latter freezes him mid-lurch but not before taking a very hard punch to the face underneath his mask.

"Sometimes the thaw brings emotional storms," says the Weatherman with great dignity as he clutches a hankie to the thin line of blood running down his neck. "You see why we wear the masks." Obviously this has happened before.

The group moves on, taking you with them. They invite you to follow them around for the day, and wherever they go, they leave a trail of infuriating pranks in their wake. Finding a ceremonial horse-guard standing stock-still, the Lookmen carefully place a dish in front of him with a few coins in it and a note attached saying 'Help our boys!' You watch as tourists step up to donate money to the mysterious military charity. Ransom runs up to a cash point and threads a scrap of paper into the notes slot, with 'I'M TRAPPED IN HERE!' written on it in letters made from chopped up tenners.

At one point they ask you to take a group photo of them, and Hijack, unnecessarily given his height, kneels down at the front for the pose. Then they gather the photo and a collection of other objects and put them in a box. Tiny Hijack, who has a surprisingly high-pitched voice, pipes: "Confound historians of the future and begin the process of change! Bury a misleading time capsule!" With considerable effort, the three anarchists manage to unscrew a manhole cover and drop in a box containing compact digital cassettes and deceptive letters extolling their virtues: "It's 2015 and everyone's still using digital compact cassettes! They are great, much better than CDs or whatever!" Between fits of delighted giggling, the group take Polaroids of themselves reading the time on a sundial. They don saucepans for hats and play biros like flutes, before labelling the photos 'The gang in contemporary costume' and stashing them in the box.

After witnessing several hours of this stuff your head is spinning. It's not clear when the show ends and normal life resumes for these people, and you're a little surprised to find yourself slightly craving cosy, unchallenging mediocrity. An entirely predictable night in with microwave lasagne and UK Gold doesn't seem so bad compared to the anxiety that would surely result from more time spent with this relentlessly anarchic band of tricksters. In a mad moment it occurs to you that you could, quite easily, kill them all. You don't even have an identity in this future, and plenty of people find them irritating. Even if anyone could be bothered to investigate the murders, surely no one would think of you...

As the sun begins to set in the dishwater sky, the Lookmen talk about returning to their headquarters.

To use the Metaphorical Attack Device, turn to page 74.

To walk with them to their car, turn to page 151.

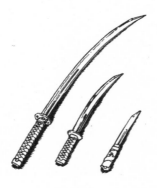

FIGHT THE GUY

There's something very satisfying about kicking a salesman in the shins and wiping that smile off his face, you discover. Suddenly sober, he backs off in astonishment, saying "What the hell are you doing?", but you ignore his protests, throwing a punch at his chin, missing, and falling flat on your face as he steps deftly to the side.

"Hold onto the card," says the Life Insurance Guy very seriously. "I can understand your suspicions, really I can. But the truth is, you're tacitly insured anyway. Against everything."

"What do you mean?"

"Awareness of death makes you feel your own life's values more keenly. Awareness of immortality makes you go round reminding people who take time to fill out quizzes on Facebook that their lives are going to end at some point."

You're still shaking your head in drunken confusion when he says, "You may be stronger than you think, but it's best you don't know too much, not yet. For now, you must be weak." He punches you hard in the stomach, and as your cries die down you hear sound of footsteps receding and the distant click of a tape recorder being switched off.

When you feel ready to stand again, you stagger across the square to a nearby shop. Turn to page 77.

GIVE THE BOX SET AWAY

You give the box set away to your box set-obsessed brother at Christmas, hoping that will be the last you hear of it. But seasonal scheduling is as poor as ever, and it's not long before someone asks if "anyone got any good DVDs for Christmas." You have overindulged on family, however, and by the time the first disk has loaded you are already pretending to be fast asleep.

Fake-sleep turns to real sleep, and when you wake on Boxing Day morning you feel nothing but the usual mixture of disappointment and relief that Christmas is over. However, things soon begin to take a turn for the strange. You snap open your laptop as usual and find yourself quite overcome by the urge look up the Wikipedia page on Wikipedia. As if the appalling post-modernism of the act wasn't sufficiently bad, as if it wasn't enough that you're staring straight into the heart of the internet, you then begin to edit the page. Since it's also true that all Wikipedia editors are ill-informed, you're effectively positioning yourself in the middle of an inescapable contradiction; but you realise all this too late – much too late – and slamming your head in the laptop doesn't seem to help. Whatever you've unleashed, it's an aggressive beast indeed. The paradox quickly spreads through grammatical slips and minor factual inaccuracies across the whole of Wikipedia, perhaps the whole internet. On top of it all, the act of looking at these sites perpetuates their existence, making it more difficult to separate the non-paradoxical from the paradoxical, effectively causing them to merge into one giant meta-paradox. Oh, what have you done?!

Vicious circles swirl around each other, the boundaries of

the accurate blurring with those of the spurious. You're caught in a logic trap set by your own fatal inquisitiveness; curiosity killed Schrödinger's cat and now you fearfully stay clear of his other pets. Before long, paradox's Escher-like fingers close around the concept of untrustworthiness itself, rendering it and everything else untrustworthy (at least that's how it seems). Nothing is reliable anymore. From a quick scroll through the ever-shifting sands of Wikipedia you learn to your surprise that the word 'dolphin' is now Latin for 'dog of the sea', that 'wi-fi' is an abbreviation of 'wience fiction', the word 'no' is the same in all languages, and that 'If you're still in a cab after 4am in Scotland, the driver has to offer you a bed for the night'. You know things have reached their nadir when you are invited to appear on the BBC's new flagship technology programme *Press*. The only logically-redundant TV show, 90% of each episode of *Press* features a camera panning slowly across the show's own website, which in turn displays mainly items from the television programme, i.e the website itself. You admit that while you may be responsible for the latest outbreak of pointless circularity, the BBC's decision to screen this kind of thing isn't helping.

Meanwhile, a generation adapted to gleaning all their information from Wikipedia is at a loss for where to go for their data and, having exhausted all the fascinating zoo-animal facts on the back of the cereal packets and those chocolate bars, turn to other, less wholesome sources for their information. A black market in 'reliable' knowledge develops off-line. People begin to turn their backs on the internet and 'libraries' housing physical books filled with information confirmed by 'experts' begin to crop up around towns.

At this point it becomes clear that the world is in a desperate regression to a definitely-inferior pre-electronic age, and you must act urgently to save it. You're too cowardly to kill yourself, but murder doesn't seem so difficult somehow, and paradox convention itself presents a suggestion. If you go back in time and kill your grandfather, you'll never be born and will never be tempted to edit the Wikipedia page about Wikipedia that created all this mess in the first place. Plus you get to kill your grandfather, whom you've never really liked very much. Ha! Paradox will ironically be its own undoing. You allow yourself a small triumphant laugh. The only problem is, you don't know how to reliably use the Entropy Phone to travel back in time. You decide to try killing your Grandad anyway, as it's your best plan – and after all it was indirectly his fault you were born and all of this came to pass. But before you even make it to his house, you are seized by a fever of existential disorientation at the checkout in Netto. Life's counter-intuitions and contradictions suddenly seem everywhere, terrifyingly inescapable. The idea that plastic bags are made out of oil is the last straw, and before you know what's happened, you've gone on a virtual killing rampage after posting a video on the actual world.

THE END

ZOMBIES ARE NERDS TOO

You hole up in the library to study the zombies from a distance, and after a week or so it becomes clear that they are obsessed with just two things: technology and their own condition. And films. The zombies are obsessed with just three things. They screen zombie movies constantly on TV and at the cinemas, critiquing them in their special late night arts review shows on BBC2 and rubbish zombie magazines (the production values are very poor but they didn't have the best start in life and are essentially homeless and disabled, so you buy them when you can).

It's as though they're trying to make some sense of it all, but lack the emotional intelligence to take responsibility for their actions. Part of you wants to hug them, and this is after having seen them and smelled them, so you can be certain it's genuine empathy. Things are getting kind of boring for you as well, living in a library with no other humans to talk to, so you go along to some of their movie screenings (arriving just after the start and leaving before the end to much irritated tutting) and, unexpectedly, it's a real eye-opener for you. It's easy to judge on initial appearances, but you challenge anyone to watch these brutes in a cinema together and fail to be deeply affected by their capacity for joy. The corpses are wonderfully free with their emotions and laugh uproariously and unselfconsciously – particularly when someone splits from the group to 'go and check things out' or a much-loved character turns out to have been hiding a scratch all along. After a couple of weeks, though, it becomes clear to you that the zombies are getting bored. And a bored zombie is a dangerous zombie.

You raid the local area for supplies and hatch a plan. There aren't any gun shops, but there is one that sells alcohol, so you barricade yourself in the library with a wall of flame made from burning books, constantly topped up with vodka. A couple of hours and Terry Pratchett's lifetime contribution to the genre later, you've made a short comedy film about zombies using the flame-wall as a backdrop and playing all the parts yourself, and uploaded it to YouTube. Within an hour of it going up, your 10-minute film has become the most popular video on the entire internet, ahead of all the previously favoured clips from *28 Days Later* and that bloke who was mistaken for an IT expert on BBC News 24*. The zombies, who all type in capitals for some reason, leave reams of badly-spelled comments on your video demanding that you make more. So this is what you do.

Whatever the problem is with their brains, it doesn't seem to have affected their technical skills. In fact, many are expert hackers, and before long they've traced your computer to your hiding place. But you're able to exploit our culture's terrible paucity of zombie-themed entertainment and the fact that YouTube is the only thing they have a more insatiable appetite

---

* You'll recall that this chap, whose name is Guy, was relatively well-known for a while in our universe too, and went on to do interviews for a number of daytime chat shows. Unfortunately, he hasn't achieved the level of fame necessary to be recognised by runners in green rooms, with the result that we've never seen the same Guy twice. In a kind of visual Chinese whispers, each runner called up the most similar-looking person to the last man mistaken for Guy, and in his later public appearances no trace of the original Guy remained.

for than brains, and quickly get a kind of arrangement going with them. So long as you keep making entertaining drunken films and uploading them to the internet, they will let you live.

It's not long before you are the only non-carnivore left on Earth. That's the surprising thing about zombies: they reproduce, and fast. Each meal creates a new zombie, and their appetite is insatiable. The rest of humankind falls within weeks, and as you sit alone behind your booze-fire performing to a webcam in the corner of an empty library, you actually begin to feel vindicated for not spending more of your life cultivating friendships. You may be alone, but you're alive. Alive, living by yourself in a library, and famous on the internet. Ha! What would the 'popular' kids think if they could see you now?

Indeed you're soon so famous that the zombies present no threat to you whatsoever. You often catch them out of the corner of your eye, snapping you with their camera phones. Braver ones sometimes approach you for an autograph, and even though you normally refuse, very rarely do they attempt to eat your brains.

Your work gets some great write-ups in the press and, despite your burgeoning alcoholism, you begin work on a hilarious one-man show about life as the final survivor in a desolate world populated by reanimated corpse automatons, and take 'Out On A Limb' to the Edinburgh Festival Fringe the same year. The zombies turn out to be the easiest crowd anyone has ever played to, loving your improvised heckler put-downs and going particularly wild for the stuff about 'not having a leg to stand on' and being 'armless'. The civilised world might have come to a devastating end, but your career has really taken an upturn.

THE END

DANGEROUS DRIVING

You walk with the troupe to their car, where everyone waits for little Hijack to catch up while pretending they're waiting for something else.

"It's not that I hate the weather now or anything," the Weatherman says to no one in particular, his sad eyes fixed on the sky. "I just wish there was a bit more of it."

The tiny man scurries up excitedly and tilts his head to look at you. "So, would you like to come back with us? We'd like you to, but you know, I can't hold a gun to your head!"

Apparently he can, and with the cold barrel against your temple, you get into the driver's seat. Before you can say "So why do they call you Hijack?" he's yelling "Just drive!" and adding "Please" and supplying the address, because you're not psychic. And as you drive, Hijack tells you how it's nice to have a break from driving, and how he used to be a London cabby before joining up with the Lookmen. Like all taxi drivers, he delights in filling an otherwise quite pleasant silence by telling you about the famous people he's had in the back of his cab. You notice, a little anxiously, that they all seem to be people who are famous principally for going missing or being eaten by cannibals. But attempting to change the subject seems to work and, at your request, Hijack fills you in on a little of the group's history.

"Many years ago," he says, "there was a troupe just like us. Not quite performers, not quite terrorists, but something in between. All had some gripe with the system. All believed in fighting the trend towards mediocrity, even if it meant they became martyrs to the cause or had to wear stupid costumes." Apparently there was a previous gang of slightly nerdy vigilantes with names like 'Static', 'Codec', 'Stargate' and 'Spellcheck', people who it seems inspired the current troupe in their endeavours. But while he's saying something about mediocrity winning out in the end in the form of a major Hollywood film based on their adventures, you sense a commotion in the back seat and check the rear-view mirror. Ransom is pulling off her mask.

"Pull over!" she says, and everyone gasps. Under the mask she's a very old lady with wire-framed glasses and a bonnet.

The Weatherman whispers in amazement, "You can speak?"

Hijack's eyes are equally wide. "You're old?"

"You fools! I am not Ransom! I captured her and stole her generic superhero costume!" More gasps. "I am the evil… I mean, I am Madame Tussaud's. I have come here because I need the Weatherman to complete my plan." She pulls out a gun and points it at Hijack, who is still holding a gun to your head. "Make him drive me to my lair at Standard Deviation Mountain!"

He's astonished. "Wait a second, have I got this right? You're hijacking me?"

There's the click of another safety catch being released, and everyone jumps and looks round to see the Weatherman holding a pistol against Madame Tussaud's's greying temple. "Make Hijack make Enemy of Chaos drive to Tussaud's's Lair at Standard Deviation Mountain," he growls.

"But that's where I want to go…" Tussaud's says cautiously.

"I know," snaps the Weatherman. "But we're going that way anyway, we can drop you off. Now, what do you say?"

After a reluctant pause, Madame Tussaud's mumbles to

Hijack, "Make Enemy of Chaos drive to Tussaud's's – my – lair at Standard Deviation Mountain."

Hijack barks, "Drive to Tussaud's's lair at –"

"Yeah. I've got it."

But you've barely been driving for ten minutes when you reach a T-junction. A sign pointing left says 'The Seaside' and one pointing the other way says 'Madame Tussaud's's Evil Lair'. You blink in surprise but there it is, in black and white.

"Go right," barks Madame Tussaud's. "Go bloody right!"

"Hey!" It's Hijack's voice. "Aren't you meant to be French?"

"Shut up!"

But the pair fall silent as the Weatherman lets out a devastating, juddering sigh. He sounds dreamy as he says, "Actually. You know what's strange? I've never seen the ocean. I'd love to see the ocean, just once."

To drive The Weatherman to the ocean, turn to page 157.
To drive to Madame Tussaud's's lair, turn to page 24.

THE JOB CENTRE

You've been exploring this middling world for an hour or so when your eye is caught by a board outside a small modern church. "Difference embraced! Join us." Your heart skips a beat; could there really be a glimmer of hope, a sign of rebellion, dissenters in the ranks? Continuing your course through mediocre suburbia it's not long before you see another, similar sign, outside the next church. This one says "Different? So are we!" under the church logo, 'The Chapel of the Holy Insurrection'. "We are more different than them," protests a third billboard outside the church across the road. "No, it is us who is the most different," insists a fourth. "That lot are all the same as each other, but we really have the edge!"

Emerging on a High Street, you see a Job Centre in front of you. As you approach, you notice the window is dominated by an 'Employment Wanted' section. For the first time, you realise all is not well with the mediocre society. The window is plastered with cards, every one a final plea from someone whose personality hasn't yet caught up with the statistical trend to mediocrity.

The employment system seems overloaded with all those who are, through skill or arrogance, unsuited to average, likely career paths. And you notice that the Job Centre is flooded with statisticians, artists and refugees from the gambling industry looking for work – in fact all those who for whatever reason need to cling to the anachronistic thought that extremes, change and comparison might all be possible, or whose livelihoods were built on the possibility that humans are special individual snowflakes.

It's clear that anyone who genuinely believes that things aren't or shouldn't be mediocre can't survive in this future. But as you scan the desperate requests, two adverts in particular catch your eye. One says, "Bad Samaritans require volunteer"; the other, "Person wanted for performances of difference."

To join the Samaritans, turn to page 94.

To call the number on the other card, turn to page 138.

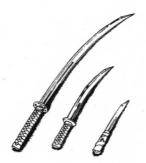

THE END OF THE LINE

The train eases to a halt.

"And now you're free," says the man who looks exactly like you and is you, as you both step off the train. Looking around, you're shocked and confused to see you are right back where you started.

"But I must return to the loop." He marches off down the platform with great ceremony before half-turning and mumbling something like, "Need the toilet first though," and nipping into the Gents.

Well, there's no doubt you're tempted to watch the DVDs. More tempted than you've ever been by anything in your life. When you're safely out of sight of the train station you throw a sidelong glance at the box set in your hand. Could you? You shake your head and turn away. No. You heard your other self: it's pure danger. To ruin your chance of protection from logical paradox just to satisfy your own curiosity would be madness. But even as you're admonishing yourself, your eyes are sneaking back over to the DVDs where they linger for a long moment. This is one decision you're not sure you can make alone. You get out the dice, rub them on your thigh, blow on them and kiss them. "Come on fellas," you say, noticing you're becoming slightly aroused. Roll the dice. Quick.

If you throw an even number, turn to page 81.

If an odd number comes up, turn to page 145.

THE TRAFFIC JAM OF ETERNITY

You hang a left, much to Madame Tussaud's's ancient annoyance, and follow the signs for the motorway. As you pull out of the slip-road you slide the car smoothly into an endless traffic jam.

"Bank Holiday Monday, of course!" Hijack bonks the gun against his head to indicate his idiocy.

"No eet eeznt," says Madame Tussaud's, who has suddenly started talking in a French accent. "Eetz Tuesday."

It is very dark outside and quite dark inside too, despite headlight beams swinging through the car as mocking vehicles speed past freely in the other direction. When you hear Hijack say in a very small voice, "Are we there yet?" you shut the engine off and thump the steering wheel with the heels of your hands. This accidentally triggers the windscreen wash, and in your haste to turn the wipers on you sound the horn.

"I said we should go right," Madame Tussaud's says quietly. The Weatherman clutches his head and slumps forward in his seat.

"Oh no. Ohno ohno ohno. I saw this coming! How could I forget?" He sounds sadder than ever. "It's The Traffic Jam of Eternity." You glance at the radio and consider putting the traffic news on.

"Aw, no. I mean, I know it feels that way right now but –"

"No, you don't understand." He sniffs hard. "Look, I see things. Okay, here goes. Lord knows we've got a while." A sardonic laugh. "Let me explain. You see, I wasn't always a weather forecaster." He finds something in his pocket and tosses it to you. Turning the object over in your hands, you recognise it as the clicker used by TV weather people to change the background image. There's a logo of some sort on it, a six-pointed star made of crossing lines. Each line terminates with an arrowhead. "It's just that there aren't that many career options for someone with my" – a pause – "abilities."

You turn round sharply at this. "Don't be alarmed," he laughs, alarmingly. "I'm what's called a Chaos Magician. It means… well, it means I can predict much more than the weather."

Hijack, Madame Tussaud's and you listen as the Weatherman explains that he's able to visualise the future based on tiny, apparently insignificant, present events. He can see time's moments unfold in glorious Technicolor all around him; observe how every instant leads to every other in all of time, forever. He says he's outside of the sequences and consequences, that he can witness the arrows of causality superimposed on our spacetime but can't influence them. He can't tell exactly when things will occur, only that they will. He says that's why he's been waiting for you, that he felt your influence long before you arrived; that you were already there in the subtle cloud stratus, the radiation frost of cold clear nights and the Rayleigh scattering of summer sunsets.

You're enraptured by his descriptions of a future you can barely begin to comprehend. This pattern of mediocrity is more damaging than any of us can imagine, he says. It will evolve and grow into the destruction of existence as we know it. With no opposing force, the mediocre era will give way to the degenerate era – he becomes quite agitated at this point, waving his arms as if in front of some electronically-generated image of the changing universe and repeatedly slapping Madame Tussaud's in the face as he mimes the equalising forces of entropy spreading across every molecule in existence. He says that this is already happening. He says that life will dissipate, liquids will turn to gas and gases will turn to heat. He says planets and moons will break apart at the very nuclei of their atoms, possibly giving way to some sunshine later on.

And then he begins to cry. In fact, the whole car begins to cry. Not the passengers, the car itself: clouds gather in the roof cavity, sounding thunderous rumbles as they collide with each other, and rain crashes violently down on the passengers with a flash of electrostatic charge.

"Oh man. We need to cheer him up," Hijack mutters, turning his collar up. "Do you want to play I Spy?" But the Weatherman will not be consoled.

"This is the Traffic Jam of Eternity. It will go on for a very, very long time. It means it's started. The…the… The Heat Death." Sniff. You ask him what he means.

"The Heat Death of the Universe has BEGUN," he shouts through the miniature thunderstorm. "It shouldn't be happening like this. And them! All those people at the front. They're rubbernecking it. They're sitting in their cars watching a wave of stars burning up and nebulae dissolving and causality itself becoming meaningless. They've slowed down to watch it, and in doing so must somehow have become part of the threshold of time itself. It's Zeno's Paradox according to Turing. It's the arrow of time, measured infinitely. The more we try to watch and measure a moment, the longer it can go on for. They've effectively frozen us in time."

Madame Tussaud's mutters, "Bastards, holding everyone else up."

"Don't you see?" He sounds calm but strangely vague, speaking almost to himself now. "This traffic jam – this is it. This is how it all ends. And how it will never end."

The rain inside the car stops and the clouds dissipate into a bone-freezing fog. After a moment, Hijack's small voice peeps cautiously out of the dampness.

"I spy with my little eye something beginning with H."

THE END

GO OUTSIDE

You head out into the sunshine through a different door to the one you came in by, and as you stand under the bright blue sky you realise for the first time that the church is in a sort of market square. There's an "Everything £1" shop to the east, and a man in a shiny suit lurking near the funeral cars.

To talk to the man, turn to page 231.
To go in the shop, turn to page 77.

THE RENEGADE POSTMAN

Alan feels along a wall in the darkness until his hand hits something, and as he pushes against it a door swings open and blinding light floods in. It's a typical suburban street, with strings of semi-detached houses and sleepy unkempt gardens. It feels early, and you decide to accompany this mysterious Renegade Postman as he goes about his unofficial business.

"There's not much time," he says, passing a letter through a swinging letterbox into the jaws of a waiting dog. "You saved my life. In return I will save yours." You ask him what he means. He sighs and parks his bike.

"There's going to be…an incident. Before I can explain that though, you should know: our country's communication networks are turmoil. We're expecting a war. A catastrophic one. Millions of people will die." He begins absentmindedly shuffling through the envelopes and whistling.

You're mildly annoyed. "Expecting a war?! How do you know?"

"When I say 'expecting' I mean it in the sense of 'starting'… Oh look, one for you!" You take the manila envelope, which has 'Enemy of Chaos, Maze, The Future' written on the front in biro, open it, and begin reading out loud.

"By the time you read this, I will be dead." You glance up. The Renegade Postman is looking sheepish. And very much alive.

"I guess I thought you'd save the girl."

"This is from you? Can't you just tell me your message?"

He leans in furtively. "We're mainly supposed to communicate using the mail system. It's like working for NatWest and banking with Barclays. Or the Post Office."

Alan explains that he's a loner, a postman unaffiliated to any team, but urges you to read the letter before he'll say any more. It is very long and detailed, containing an impressive amount of data about the history of the UK's mail service. You find yourself drawn in. The postman stands patiently watching as you learn that the Post Office was first established in 1939 to provide a network of local outposts of the Home Office. Unable to decide whether it was principally an outPOST or a Home OFFICE, they took their title from both – hence the potentially tautological brand that would become so familiar.

But everything changed with the 1979 home delivery revolution: suddenly the world was just a phonecall away. Milkmen continued to go door-to-door with their deliveries just as they always had, but now they were followed on their rounds by float-driving sugarmen and teamen. With this kind of competition on the rise, nobody was impressed by the idea of the inefficient, uncool postal service any more and simply stopped bothering to send thank-you notes to elderly relatives until the phenomenon of physical mail almost died out entirely, along with the elderly relatives.

The Post Office and its regal aunt the Royal Mail were stripped of funds, dignity and many of their motorised vehicles. While endless exciting advances in communications were enjoyed by the rest of the world, the UK's mail delivery service looked like it was going to be insulated from progress and remain a museum to 1970s beige technologies for the rest of time. Indeed some Post Offices did manage to capitalise on their misfortune and rake in a little extra cash by opening on Sundays as museums of vintage technology.

Yet, despite the obvious handicaps – not least their effective exclusion from the internet age and email – postal workers continued to carry out their rounds with admirable conscientiousness, delivering more and more unlikely things to increasingly difficult destinations just to keep themselves and their work viable in the age of the internet. For many, though, this determination to stick to routine and reluctance to adapt to the times was their downfall.

Two competing services emerged as the main contenders, battling it out for the country's dwindling mail opportunities. With postcode districts shrinking all the time, The Occupiers and The Senders became embroiled in an extraordinarily relentless and imaginative one-upmanship in their battle for the remaining postcodes. The Occupiers' location was on record as "House Name/Address 1/Address 2/Postcode", while The Senders operated from specially modified rural cottages until the dissolution of the Post Offices in 2007, at which point many postal workers became essentially itinerant.

Thus The Occupiers and The Senders have spent the last three decades trying to outdo one another. In an escalating determination to deliver earlier than their enemy, officers rose earlier and earlier until letters were being shoved through doors shortly before they'd been written, whereupon they were pushed back out of the letter box and caught in the postman's other hand. Competitiveness is the mother of invention, however, and there's no doubt that both sides achieved extraordinary feats of postal delivery during the Mail Wars of the early 21st century – though inevitably both overstretched themselves at times, and had their judgments clouded by superstition. One employee refused to allow his fatally damaged red van to be repaired, insisting he was "taking mail to Heaven"; another was tragically misunderstood attempting to deliver a baby. And one day The Occupiers cornered the market on the Earth's core. They never found their way out again and the rest, as they say, is history. Unfortunately it's history you don't know, so you ask the Renegade Postman to explain.

Turn to page 120.

SAY NO

"Not really," you say. "Sorry."

"Well," the Undertaker snaps back on after a few frantic flashes. He reminds you of a strip light. "Just between us, it doesn't matter that much whether you grasp the details of the problem or not. All you need to know is things are bad for the Fantasy Universe. You're our only hope. So, you know, don't cock it up."

"B-b-but am I in the Fantasy Universe or the real, physical one?"

The Undertaker winces. "NEVER talk to VICTIM members about the 'real' universe. Reality is relative!"

You make a mental note.

"The thing people don't realise is," he goes on, "the Fantasy Universe plays host to the one you call 'real', not the other way around. The Entropy Phone can take you to fantastical places but this doesn't mean you won't come to harm. Because the Fantasy Universe is the most dangerous world of all. Especially since the Games Master –" he stops himself. "Well, you know."

You do know. The Undertaker suggests you head outside to pick up some supplies before you get started on your quest.

Turn to page 161.

STAYING PUT

When the new Order has finished homogenising people, it begins to spread to the outside world. Buildings shift on their foundations to become more symmetrical, and align themselves on the street in order of price, causing endless neighbourly rifts but taking some of the legwork out of house-hunting. Sudokus leap from the hands of commuters and resolve themselves. Foodstuffs placed on the same plate proudly refuse to touch each other, and certain colours disappear entirely from the visible spectrum. Everywhere you look you see yourself reflected back, and everywhere you go has a strangely sensible, off-kilter beauty. You're inhabiting a nightmare landscape perfectly designed for you. If hell is other people, heaven is the same person: you. You, you, you and you, over and over again.

But not everyone is happy. In this dogmatic new world, systems prevail over individuals, and millions of people are killed in what will one day be wryly dubbed 'The Magnitude of Order'. Martial law is enforced to protect the few survivors, and since the roads have rearranged themselves in a perfect fractal curve around your hotel room, it doesn't take long for the army to work out who's responsible. You're thrown into jail for the rest of your life but have never been happier. Alone in a symmetrical cell, you count and recount the bars and even come to enjoy the methodical physical labour involved in the prisoner's chores, such as breaking long URLs down into small ones and making sure the right chocolates are in the right holes in Marks & Spencer advent calendars.

With no distractions and a wonderfully reliable routine, you find prison to be the perfect environment for your suppressed character traits to thrive. You persuade the guards to let you have a piano, and left to your own devices you happily while away the lonely nights playing elaborate concertos you've only ever read reviews of, sometimes pausing to draw incredibly accurate diagrams of buildings you once heard someone describe on the radio.

THE END

THE BAD SAMARITANS III

It rings again.

"Sorry," you say. "I panicked."

He laughs a hollow, worrying laugh. You're not sure you like this old you. He speaks softly in a tired voice and from what he says, you gather he's been alone for a very long time. Perhaps it's inevitable that he has started to go a bit strange. Worse, it's not clear which parts of his incredible story you should believe and which are merely the lively creations of a senile imagination. When he says, "I can hear voices on the line," and you tell him no, they're in his head, he gasps with relief. "Oh! Thank God!"

More significantly, though, he advises you to get off the phone and call the number on the other card – it's your best shot. Future-future you won't go into specifics but says simply that if you choose not to follow his advice then, one day when the time is right, you'll need to phone yourself up at the Samaritans and tell yourself not to listen to yourself. Then, just as you begin to ask, "Are you aware that you've been talking about yourself in the third pers–" the line goes quiet. You try tapping the receiver against the table and holding it back up to your ear, but for some reason that makes no difference. No. It's no good, you've gone.

To follow your advice, turn to page 138.

To ignore your advice – whatever happens, happens – turn to page 43.

CONTINUE

The text carries on on a new screen.

> In a moment, a list of arcade games will load.
> Select 'Pac-man'. If you can get past the
> third level and enter your initials on the
> scoreboard using the annoying joystick alphabet
> scroll*, then statistical acceleration will
> occur. You will be transported into a very
> different world – a mysterious future world
> beyond your imagination. A world, perhaps,
> where everything that can happen will happen.
> Who knows? Not us. You're the adventurer.
> Sake.
>
> You have five minutes. Slay those ghosties
> now! V. (PS Despite manufacturer's claims that
> the monsters all travel at the same speed,
> everyone knows the pink one is slightly faster
> than the others so watch out for him.)

Pac-man turns out to be just as playable as you remember it
being, and you sail through the first couple of levels easily. At
the three and a half-minute mark, Pinky really pulls out the stops

---

*   As everyone knows, all the best games are themed around tedious physical
    labour to some extent (Manic Miner, Chuckie Egg, Lemmings, Dig Dug…)
    and the game of life is no different. Boring, repetitive and full of arbitrary
    achievement thresholds.

and things begin to look a little shaky, but you stick it out. Three minutes forty. Three fifty-five. At four minutes, the screen goes wobbly. Then you realise: it's not the screen. It's your eyes. And the screen. And your eyes.

Turn to page 134.

USE THE GRAPHIC RANDOMISER

The Graphic Randomiser comes in a small velvet bag with 'How long does now last?' written on one side, and 'A bit' on the other. Which is a low-grade pun, because 'one bit' is of course the information entropy of a statistically fair coin, whose tosses eventually even out at a round 50/50. What's in the bag, however, is a decidedly unfair coin whose effects on time and space potentially expand far beyond anything anyone would reasonably describe as 'a bit'.

The device was invented by the same giant brain that created 'Graphic Equalisers' so beloved of CD Walkmans in the early 90s, and it has about as much to do with graphics. Its designers seem to have been working on the bold and unsupportable assumption that, as physical currency becomes redundant, money will be measured less in terms of its financial value and more and more in terms of its probability flip – how often a heads and a tails is likely to occur.

When the two states are equally likely, statistical randomness results – a simple fact that has no value. But this kind of randomness ultimately creates a moderate and universally acceptable situation of banal happy-clappy even-handedness where committee decision rules and, ironically enough, nothing unexpected ever happens. These are the rules to which regular coins are beholden, the rules that brought you here to this world of moderate averageness.

The Graphic Randomiser, on the other hand, is a right

bastard of a coin. It is the opposite of the Statistical Accelerator, in fact the opposite of any equalising force. You look at the gleaming newly-minted currency in your hand and wonder at its possibilities. You slightly fear it too, because what you're holding is a not simply an object powered by the fearful determination of extreme whim, it's a beast. A monster that feeds off and kills statistics. The Graphic Randomiser shamelessly hates what is likely and mocks what is probable.

A normal coin flip reinforces sameness because it has an ultimate path, a mysterious mathematical likeliness tendency. Its motivations are perceived as far beyond our human knowledge. A normal coin is subject to destiny. The Graphic Randomiser, however, can effect change. It has no respect for predestination, gets by with only one side, and, flipped with a blank mind, can overturn all previous assumptions about the world.

You rest the coin on the back of your thumb and with a deft motion send it spinning high into the air. Time seems to slow down as you watch the coin twist and turn and somersault against a backdrop of smoggy rooftops.

Although you can't see it, the Graphic Randomiser's effects are rippling out from the coin to the whole neighbourhood as it spins, and for the few seconds it takes to complete its arc, anything can – and does – happen. A routine laser eye procedure becomes semantically confused with a tattoo removal operation, resulting in both patients receiving laser eye removal. As internet CAPTCHAs make the leap to the real world, a customs desk insists that aspiring travellers can only pass if they can prove they are human by repeating a complicated sequence of bizarre noises with their voice. A nearby pet shop starts tagging its animals with scannable implants that can only be removed at the till with keyhole surgery. Cash machines finally decide to liven up the withdrawal process by coyly declaring they 'may' charge for withdrawals, and customers take their chances.

Time accelerates, warps and buckles in pulses with the coin at the centre, causing some nearby homes to lose years while others gain decades. In one house, the information contained in an overdue library book is released gradually over months and years and reabsorbed by the other books on the shelf. When it is eventually returned to the library after an interval of 43 years, it is entirely useless.

Professor Stephen Hawking, who is visiting a relative not far away, finds his inner thoughts have suddenly been rendered audible by his speech synthesiser. Since his thoughts can only be silenced by Leona Lewis's beautiful single 'Bleeding Love', the Professor is forced to take up permanent residence in a helicopter hovering over Cambridge, where no one can be bothered by his music. And at a police station down the road, suspects taken in for questioning are allowed one wish instead of one phone call, as long as they don't go for 'infinite wishes'*.

Then the coin comes hurtling down again; you catch it and slap it hard onto the back of your knuckles. Peeling your hands apart you look at the shining disk, and there, where the Queen's head should be, a picture of a snowflake has appeared.

"What does this mean?" you ask the coin, which says nothing. Because, at the end of the day, it's still a coin.

---

* Infinity is overrated anyway. It's worth remembering that finite wishes are usually more than sufficient for most mortals, if a sufficiently large number is selected.

Things certainly livened up there for a while, but, just like the graphic equalisers that preceded it, the Graphic Randomiser is one of those Innovations catalogue gimmicks that felt essential one Christmas but can make no measurable difference to anything in the long term and whose energies soon fade away. With a whole bank full of these, maybe you'd start to see some real change; but as it is, you and your coin are overpowered by a global tide of mediocrity.

Spending Graphic Randomiser coins can be difficult because of their insistence on only being used for things its owner really wants, deep down. Indeed, the coin won't settle for anything less than the dream, the platonic ideal, and will cling stubbornly to the spender's fingertips until the perfect item is found. You dip in and out of shops, holding it up to everything, but it won't budge. In the mediocre future, the trend for weekend newspapers to give away increasingly rubbish and worthless gifts has reached its natural conclusion, and although it is understandably resistant to the idea of you spending it on a paper that promises 'free news', the coin does allow you to use it as insurance on a shopping trolley when you need to do a quick Tesco shop later.

Turn to page 154.

SEE HOW THINGS PAN OUT

You hide in the shop, surviving on family-sized chocolate bars which, reckoning you should maintain some semblance of civilisation, you sell to yourself for the bargain price of £1[*] with each newspaper you buy. While you're safely hiding and steadily gaining weight, a nuclear winter descends outside. To start with, it is a dark and frightening time. Temperatures drop, crops fail, epidemics spread like wildfire which spreads like the plague. With most satellites knocked out by nuclear blasts, the country is thrown into a new Dark Ages where travellers must resort to using their eyes to navigate on car journeys, TV channel numbers are down to 1988 levels and the next day's weather can only be guessed at. Plumes of toxic smoke twist in the foul wind over desecrated cities. The very fabric of civilisation starts to shred as people no longer want to play by society's so-called rules. Water supplies are fatally polluted by radiation and dissidents who deliberately neglect to shower before entering the swimming pool. Food poisoning is rife due to a lack of qualified public health inspectors. With soil unusable, farmers dead and machinery decayed, modern agriculture is no longer possible. Victorian farming museums, however, come into their own as the nation finally has a reason to listen to someone dressed in a sack talk in a fake rustic accent about wheelwrighting.

But humans are surprisingly resilient, and it's not long before

---

[*] It's an interesting fact that one in 40 pound coins is a worthless fake, not recognised by British authorities. By coincidence, the Isle of Man mint produces about 2.5% of the coins in circulation in the UK today.

survivors begin to ask if global thermonuclear war really is the disaster everyone had it pegged for, and whether we shouldn't, in fact, stand back from the destruction of everything our race has been achieved in the last 200,000 years and try to see it as a new beginning. After a month or so many manage to look on the bright side, even coming to enjoy the unexpected time off work. Apparently bored of reporting on Soviet counterstrikes, the BBC News website holds a competition for the best nuclear fallout snowman. There are a lot of emails going around with lists of 'nuke gags', too. Some people say that with half the population of the planet dead or dying and civilisation as we know it obliterated, these jokes are in bad taste and you should stop sending them. But you think it's important to try to keep a sense of humour about what's happened.

Turn to page 197.

ALTERNATIVE ENDING

"Not too simple," you reply quickly. "Not at all too simple. Just simple enough."

"Good. So that's why I need you." She rounds on the Weatherman. "One day I'll be out of cryoagents, but you! You can freeze people where they stand! And you!" Her eyes bore holes in you. "Your knowledge of science will resurrect them when we're done!"

The Weatherman pushes one sleeve up and declares "Is that the time?" but as he begins to back away, Tussaud's roars:

"No one's going ANYWHERE!" and clicks her fingers. Suddenly four vertical bars of buzzing light appear from nowhere, the cornerposts of some kind of electrical enclosure penning the Weatherman. The tall man's face contorts as he realises, aghast, that he's trapped in a humming cubicle – an invisible cage. With one hand cautiously extended, he tries to touch the screen in front of him, but immediately snatches his long fingers back as though they're burned. You can hear his muffled shouts through the forcefield – mainly "Let me out," but also the occasional "This is how Marcel Marceau died you know!" Tussaud's turns away from him and looks at you with eerie calm.

"You're all mine now."

"Till when?" squeaks Hijack, craning his head up at the old woman.

"As long as it takes. I'll find work for all the mighty Lookmen. And you as well." She looks at Hijack. "Things are good for us. This mediocre age has been a boom time for my museums."

"EVEN THE PLANETARIUM?" shouts the Weatherman

from his invisible cage and everyone winces.

"I knew he'd bring that up," Life Insurance Guy mutters.

"Yes, alright, the Planetarium is a lost cause," admits Tussaud's. "But we have some fantastic new stars coming to the wax museum this summer." She nods approvingly as she lists them. "Richey Edwards. Fearne Cotton. David Blaine. Donnie Darko." Hijack narrows his eyes.

"Those are all people," he says slowly, "who've gone missing..."

"Ah, you heard! Anyway it's not just us of course." She brightens. "There are other average tourist attractions too, all waiting to reopen for the summer season. Speaker's Corner will continue to disappoint visitors from around the world. Miniature villages everywhere will be less exciting than any visitors imagined. Somewhere in Cornwall a collection of taxidermal rodents in school uniforms will elicit more mild disgust than curiosity from its rain-soaked Bank Holiday guests. The mediocre competition is strong but Tussaud's will prevail because it will literally have a captive audience for all time!" She presses a button on the wall and the floor lights up with a bright white square. PowerPoint starts to run through a series of slides on the smooth floor and projected images of liquid nitrogen chambers, chemistry diagrams and equations flash past quickly in front of your feet.

"I've been working on this cryonics technology for many years, and now my perfect visitors will stay perfect forever! Imagine their beautiful, beautiful stillness. Tussaud's will prevail! Oh, I already said that." The post-cog's lips have turned blue. You wonder if it's too late to do something.

"Any questions?" She glares at each of you in turn.

"I have a question," says Hijack.

"Anyone else?" Tussaud's asks hopefully. Hijack starts asking if it's 'cryonics' or 'cryogenics' but Tussaud's just shakes her head and turns to her pre-cogs, still bobbing in the pool.

"My time has come at last!" And as she throws back her head a terrifying cackle escapes. Unfortunately, it's the only thing that does. You live out your days in the employment of Madame Tussaud's, working on an antidote for the cryostasis process and helping the Weatherman to freeze abducted minor celebrities on the insane whim of a mad stillness-obsessed old woman.

THE END

PHONE THE LIFE INSURANCE GUY

You go to a payphone and get the card out of your pocket. No contact details! How could you forget? But as you turn to leave there's a ring. A ring-ring. A ring-ring ring-ring. You give the telephone a suspicious look, then cautiously pick up the receiver.

"Hello?" you whisper.

"Who is this?" It's a strident male voice.

"Erm, h-h-how did you get this number?"

"I asked you first."

"I'm the Enemy of Chaos."

"Emily who? It's Frozen Assets. I'm laughing in the face of your family's bereavement as we speak. You requested a call? What can I do for you?"

"I think there is about to be a mass catastrophic event," you say. "I need to know you have my back."

"Ooh, really? Thanks for the heads up. I'll get down to the bunker."

"Wait! Am I alright?"

"Sorry," he says. "No time to chat." And he's gone.

Turn to page 54.

WHERE DO WE GO FROM HERE?

"Fine. End of the world. But you'll still have to buy that," snaps the shopkeeper, when your vision begins to return. As you search for change in your pocket you're filled with a sense of awe, noticing that, even with everyone on the planet annihilated, the shopkeeper has still found someone to talk on his mobile when he's supposed to be serving you. Your Entropy Phone, meanwhile, seems to have been knocked out of action altogether...

To stay where you are, turn to page 176.

To head into the street and seek shelter with the first person you meet, turn to page 195.

FRIENDS FOREVER

You don't have many friends, at least not real ones. But one man's Armageddon is another's Revelations, and now that the world has been overrun by antisocial habit-loving technophiles you'd be a fool not to seize this once-in-a-lifetime opportunity to build some kind of social life. It takes a while to gain their trust, but over the coming months you grow quite close to the zombies. The small internet community that survives embraces the walking dead for their simple and straightforward motivations. Indeed, they have many qualities that endear them to you: their inability to lie, their conscientious pursuit of a goal and their impossible clumsiness, to name just three. Often mocked as herd-like creatures, the absence of individual ego can be interpreted as a charming lack of self-awareness. The zombies are not a complicated people but their view of the world is none the worse for that. You feel comfortable being around them. In fact, you feel as though you already know them somehow.

And so it is that you start by playing World of Warcraft with them, gradually securing your place in the group and eventually arranging to meet some of them in real life. "Let's meet up," you type, after one particularly devastating raid. "BRAINS," they reply, mysteriously. In fact, the zombies don't say much at all – like you, they're creatures of few words. Well, just one, really. But as long as sudden movements and direct eye contact can be avoided, I think they'll survive you.

THE END

UP ON THE ROOF

You find a staircase and cautiously make your way to the flat roof of the library as quietly as possible so as not to arouse the attention of any nearby zombies and also out of respect for other tax-paying users of the facility. Climbing out onto the fire escape at the top of the building, the first thing you notice is the groaning. The next is the smell. You take a good look around before resolving to have a shower tonight, and your gaze falls on the street below. As you watch, shuffling hordes of decaying corpses advance on a house opposite the library, clawing at the windows with their ghoulish hands. There are about 109 of them, you guess, if you count from zero, which of course you do. After a couple of minutes a side door swings open and the creatures stop still, before slowly – very, very slowly – turning to look.

An old man walks calmly into his front garden and stops, his head bowed.

"NO!" Your arms fly out instinctively. But it's too late. They're closing in on him, severed limb against protruding bone, creaking corpses knitting together like a big scarf of death. Unspeakable globules of purple-red goo fling out in a grim centrifuge from the foetid scrum and you wince at every awful squelchy crunch. Eventually the creatures retreat and stagger off towards the next house leaving the bloodied remains of their victim face down on the grass.

But then – no! How can it be? You watch in amazement as he starts to get up on his feet, apparently unscathed. When he turns towards you his face – what's left of it – is inscrutable, skin hanging in flaps from his chin like jolly bunting. For a brief moment he catches your eye and smiles up at you with both his mouths, but then he's gone, lost in the crowds.

Turn to page 199.

BREAKING NEWS

You look up "zombies" and "apocalypse" on the computer, and the first non-death-metal website that comes up is an article on the *Guardian*'s 'Comment is Free' page. The title is "Who's the enemy here?"

> Traditional literature recommends trying to destroy these monsters, but rarely has anyone stopped to ask whether that's the only option. No one seems to have thought about why cannibalistic corpses are suddenly roaming the planet. No one has, if you'll excuse the expression, attempted to get inside their heads. This is a damning indictment of our quick-fix society: we're so trigger happy when it comes to the zombie 'problem' that we're not thinking long-term. If we weren't at each other's throats (again, sorry) all the time, we might have a chance of recognising the real victims in all of this. They are our present, and they may well be our future. I believe the question is not how we can, but whether we should in fact attempt to 'kill' the dead at all.

The author's obituary is linked from their name at the bottom. They're running a poll, too: "Should waking dead be made to carry ID cards?" Meanwhile the *Daily Mail* website leads with "Labour blunders into End Times". The piece begins: "Immigrants cost the tax-payer £2million per year EACH per minute EVERY HOUR. As house prices plummet to

BASICALLY FREE, today's apocalypse proves beyond doubt that we should hate everything". *The Sun* has a zombie Page 3 girl called Amanda and *The Weekly World News* is running a story about President Obama's latest efforts at tacking the global recession.

To follow the Mail and look out for number one, turn to page 34.

To reach out to them as the Guardian suggests, turn to page 183.

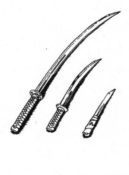

CARRY ON DOCTOR

You rush back to the hospital but it's already too late. The place has become a zombie hotbed. Hospitals are, after all, stuffed with people with weak immune systems who can't easily get away, not to mention offal, predictable routines, soap operas and the unbearable stench of death – all of the things that zombies, in common with the elderly, famously love. The creatures are so well-served by the NHS, in fact, that it's a wonder they ever bother with hostile places like the Blackwall Tunnel.

Faced with the prospect of fatal zombie attack and with nowhere to hide, you do the only thing you can. The noble thing. You disguise yourself as a corpse and hide in the hospital's morgue. It's not great in the morgue, although, thinking about it rationally, you're not sure what you were expecting really. There's a chill in the air and a weird chemical smell, but at least since the whole dead-people-rising thing there are plenty of spare beds to choose from. You find it's possible to observe the creatures' behaviour from a distance. The zombies come and go constantly, but they have no upper body strength at all and it takes them at least half an hour to claw open the fire door. You consider building them a flap of some sort just to make the terrible scratching noise stop. In fact, at times it becomes so unbearable that you have to jump up and get the door for them.

Their behaviour fascinates you to begin with, so human and yet…so other. But after witnessing one using the autopsy scales to weigh its 'human groceries' one time too many, you decide the time has come to find a new place to live.

Venturing out into the world is a big step. Luckily the zombies surrounding the hospital are well-fed and when you avoid eye-contact and mimic their movements as best you can, they don't seem to notice you shuffling past. The first thing that strikes you is the way the creatures have already divided themselves into two groups. There are the 'First Generation' zombies – that is, those who have risen from graves through the mysterious entropy-reversing effect of your Rubric's Cube – and the 'Second Generation', those whose condition has arisen from a bite or scratch, and as such are considered spurious, somehow less 'true' or authentic than the original kind. The first generation prefer to lounge around in graveyards like goths on holiday, prostrate in the grass with their arms bent behind their heads. They mostly come out at night. Mostly. While the 'nouveau deceased', their seniors maintain, have only been around five minutes and as such have no appreciation for the finer things in death. Still they seem content to ponce off the intimidating reputation of the first generation without ever having experienced what it's like to decompose. In a quite literal sense, they don't know they're dead.

It is something of a relief to discover that, despite their apparently insurmountable disadvantages, the creatures have retained their sense of humour, though it does seem to be somewhat simple-minded and based on wordplay. You spot one selling sympathy cards in bulk on a market stall, and you almost laugh when you see that a nearby coffee shop has already had its sign deftly altered to read 'Caffè Necro' by some expired culture-jamming wag.

A poster in the window of the Starbucks next door to 'Necro' asks: "WHO CAN HAZ OUR VOICE?" in large, red, suspiciously drippy letters. You head inside with caution, taking care not to make eye contact with any of the zombies, who are sitting around mumbling to each other or absent-mindedly rocking pushchairs while their zombie children gallop up and down the diminishing floor area, screaming.

Turn to page 38.

STARBUCKS: THE EX GENERATION

You attempt to fight the zombies, but it's clear they're more interested in trying to get onto a wireless network without having to pay for the extortionate coffee shop wireless prices. So instead you head outside, where you find an abandoned internet café.

The place has clearly been empty for a while; perhaps the previous owners overestimated the national demand for single-use phone cards. But the technology still seems to work and, sensing a business opportunity, you print out some signs making sure to include plenty of free clip-art of steaming coffee mugs to differentiate yourself from the competition. You enable pop-ups on all browsers and fill the desktops with weird chat clients that no one uses anymore before setting them to load as soon as anyone presses a key. If you can lure them in with rock-bottom hourly internet rates, budget printing and the enticingly dangerous combination of hot beverages and expensive electronic equipment, you might just be able to keep these creatures distracted long enough to buy you the time to come up with a better plan.

You don't have much competition, apart from the Starbucks that suddenly appears on the other side of the road a week after you open, and on the whole your ploy works. Straggling groups of staggering zombies are drawn to the café to check their emails and attempt to make long-distance phone calls even though it's prohibitively expensive, everyone can hear their conversations, the computers all have Skype and headphones, they can't speak properly and the population of the world is dead.

All of the creatures suffer from a degree of amnesia as a result of their brains being starved of oxygen during death, and most can't remember much about the internet, so it's not long before you become an invaluable resource to them. They don't realise it, but the best internet you're able to offer is a very slow, very limited, and very out-of-date one, with the only real updates being done by you (it looks like most of the rest of the world has been wiped out). You feel protective towards your regulars, though – they seem oblivious to what's happened and appear to see you more as part of the equipment than as a tasty meal – so you exploit their need for routine by inventing daily world news and uploading it to a special www.news.bbc.co.org.uk site.

You watch them as they come in every day and sit down at your crappy computers to read the news you made up that morning just for them, and you can't help being moved by the sight. It's not fear any more, but pity that you feel for these creatures who have no idea of the extent of their affliction and remember nothing of their former lives. They devour the information you feed them and watch in wide-eyed amazement as you 'cure' their laptops and phones by plugging them into the mains for half an hour.

Turn to page 55.

A MESSAGE FROM VICTIM:

When you arrive at the Arcade, only one machine seems to be working. There's a message flashing on the screen in a monospaced OCR font. You wiggle the joystick and a tinny electronic fanfare sounds from the depths of its ancient speakers.

```
***** Congratulations from VICTIM!!!! *****
```

Well done Enemy of Chaos! According to the signal emitted by your Entropy Phone, you have completed Level 1 of your mission. You have successfully imposed a sense of order where none previously existed.

We are reaching out to you now because Fate has spoken. What Fate says is that upgrades are now available for your Entropy Phone and it will restart automatically in four minutes. In order to upgrade the device and progress to Level 2, please read the following.

First of all, you must sign in. VICTIM promises not to pass your personal details on to third parties, but if anyone happens to see them by accident it isn't our fault.

The message continues on a new screen. There are two options:

"To view the science lecture, press the red button. To CONTINUE, press the yellow button."

The machine has two big round brightly-coloured buttons on the top, and your fingers hover over them as you make your choice.

To carry on, turn to page 170.

To divert to the science lecture, turn to page 115.

GHOST WORLD

It's a dangerous world out there – too dangerous to go outside for at least a few weeks – so you head down to the city's sewer system. After what feels like miles of wading and splashing through the filthy underground river, a distinct sobbing sound cuts through the sickening sewer gurgle. And there she is. Slumped behind some pipes, knee-deep in bubbling sewage, a young girl is crying. She stops abruptly when she sees you.

"Oh great." She actually groans.

"Are you OK?" You're experimenting with empathy.

"I swear I didn't do it."

"What?"

"That." She points directly up. "I didn't make that bomb go off."

"Why would you think that?"

"I don't. I didn't. Think what?" Guilt flashes across her face, but she holds up her phone before you have a chance to speak. "Anyway it might as well be the end of the world 'cos my phone's fucked. I can't get a fucking signal."

"I might be able to help," you offer.

She hands you her mobile and pulls that face that women pull when someone else is holding their baby and they want to look casual about it but really they just want you to die so they can get it back. You examine the phone, but she's right. It's fucked.

"It's bad, isn't it?" she says, as you return it to her.

"Bad as in… good?" You're never sure.

"Wow," she gasps. "Just how old are you?"

You wipe a hand on your trousers and hold it out.

"Good to find another survivor."

"Thanks, Grandad."

The girl who may or may not have somehow been the final straw in the sequence of events leading to nuclear apocalypse shows you a passageway up a waste disposal system that leads into a five star hotel in central London. Things are okay to begin with, but after a few weeks holed up in a hotel room with a much younger woman and no DVDs to watch except *Leon, American Beauty, Taxi Driver* and *Ghost World*, you find that the risk of dying of radiation poisoning outweighs the embarrassment of staying where you are. So it is that, one day, you decide it is time to leave. Just like Captain Oates before you, you have no intention of returning, and turning to the girl for the last time you utter the immortal words "I'm just going outside. Do you want anything?" before closing the door behind you and venturing into the post-nuclear wastelands alone.

To see what's down the street, turn to page 67.

To look for more appropriate survivors, turn to page 222.

MONEY PROBLEMS

The collapse of the world economy and the increasing scarcity of essential resources lead to a new bartering system based on valuable commodities. Those with ready access to ammunition, gold and diamonds, such as royalty, are immediately invested with the power of kings. The rest of the world watches them bitterly, as it hopes to raise the resources for a crust of bread with jewellery looted from a ram-raided Cards Galore. And after a few years, when it becomes clear that land is so plentiful and polluted that it has no worth at all, the Royal Family begins to lose its power to impress an increasingly disenchanted nation. In a world without the Games Master's influence, it seems chaos is indeed triumphing once again, and as one of the brightest survivors, it falls to you to come up with a new use for the monarchy.

Roll two dice.

If you roll a 6 or below, wait a few years — this is just a temporary event relating to the immediate consequences of nuclear disaster — turn to page 204.

If you roll a 7 or above, congratulations — you're giving the Royal Family a new career in showbusiness. Turn to page 207.

SHE LIKES YOU MORE

The travel agent lies down on the floor and pats the carpet next to her, sending up a cloud of radioactive dust.

"I'm Andi?" You're unsure how to answer. "Come here?" she says, still patting. It's probably just Australian Question Intonation, you reason, and deciding there can be no good way of responding to that, you lie down beside her with undisguised reluctance.

"Now. Say you've got the time." She's excited. "Go on!" It isn't infectious.

"I've got...the time?" you falter.

"I've got the space!" She reaches over to the wall and a moment later the room is flooded with blackness. Steadily, one by one, smaller lights wink on across the ceiling. Then the walls, then the floor and the space in front of your eyes until you can't tell where you are or which way is up anymore. Some of the lights glow more fiercely than others, some are coloured rich reds and golds, and several are ringed with countless tiny particles of dust and ice. It's incredible – the time travel agent has transformed the place into a dazzling planetarium. You look around open-mouthed at the pinprick stars, nebulae, and distant galaxies, all wonderfully realised, all alive and in motion around you. A shooting star arcs directly above your heads and the travel agent lets a pure childlike laugh escape. You look at her smiling sideways face lit by starlight and you feel...nothing.

"So," she whispers. "Where would you like to go?"

Turn to page 210.

HAVE A LOOK AROUND

Your eyes wander to a group of kids on a street corner. They're pale, listless and blank-eyed with ragged clothing that barely covers their scrawny forms. In fact they're just like normal teenagers. But these are no normal teenagers; from certain angles it is possible to see what's behind them without asking them to move. And then you realise: they're texting.

With a shudder of fear you can't help but think: did I lock my car? Then: if they can text, what else can they do? And who the hell are they texting anyway? Catching up with pals they haven't seen since lunch, no doubt. Boredom appears to be as much of a problem for the passed-on as it was for living youngsters.* You briefly consider teaching them some chords on the guitar, but see sense just in time.

As quietly as you can, you climb down to the High Street and find an electronics goods shop, its windows lined with television sets. But every channel seems to be showing the same thing: scenes of groaning hordes with missing limbs and carnage. Such terrible carnage. You let out an involuntary gasp as it occurs to you that this must be a global phenomenon. But as you watch the creatures trip and scrape down country lanes and heave themselves from graves with toothpick fingers, two further thoughts hit you. Firstly: whatever these creatures are, they have

---

* Statistically more children die of texting while crossing roads than of zombie bites, though crossing zombie roads can be fatal in a different way, depending on zombie speed restrictions (the walk, stagger or run debate rages on).

control of all the channels, even Nickelodeon. And secondly: on every channel – every single one – they're showing zombie films.

It's worse than you'd dare to imagine. How these monsters function is now the least of your worries and for the first time you really understand why the scientific details have never been properly addressed in zombie fiction. With control of the world's media the creatures have real power over the trends influencing a generation of impressionable youngsters. And although there's certainly a sense in which this could be considered to be your fault, it also strikes you that TV's ongoing glamorisation of violence should really take some of the rap for what has happened. And computer games as well.

To find their weakness, turn to page 148.
To read the news, turn to page 186.

THERE'S ONLY ROOM FOR ONE POSTMODERNIST IN THIS DAMN PUNCTUATION MAZE

You pick up an enormous asterisk and lob it at them, but it misses, instead striking a nearby underscore and ricocheting off an @. The @ is about 10 feet high and the three of you watch in horror as it begins to topple onto the role players. Their torches lick at the polystyrene as it descends, and the shape quickly becomes a fireball heading for their flammable heads.

"Wait!" the man cries. "I know something, something you'll need if you're to escape from this place!"

"Er, me too!" says the woman. "A different thing! Pick me!"

"She's had her life!" screams the man. "I'm the one you need!"

At this the woman shouts, "My God Alan, if we get out of this alive I'm going to kill you!"

"Argh! It's about to hit us!" the man yells, his face aghast.

"Don't change the subject!" she wails back.

The @ continues to tumble, and you only have time to save one of them...

To save the man, turn to page 114.
To save the woman, turn to page 83.

AMAZING GAMES

You send the text and when the light subsides you find yourself in some kind of dim windowless space with a low ceiling. The path immediately to your right is blocked by a wall slightly taller than you and about six feet wide. Its edges are turned in, to create the effect of a three-dimensional square bracket. You then discover another one to your left, also facing inwards. And at the point where you're standing, halfway between the two giant brackets, there's a sign on the wall saying [you are here]. You allow yourself a moment of unbridled screaming panic before getting a grip, and soon find that the brackets move quite easily; they look heavy but seem to be made of polystyrene. A glance around confirms that the rest of the underground area is divided by more of this giant three-dimensional punctuation – a curly bracket here, a hyphen there. At one point you even spot an exclamation mark!

Weaving your way further through the arbitrarily delineated space, you think you begin to hear male and female voices. And as you step out from under a suspended apostrophe and into the shadowy perimeter of a small clearing, you see a man and a woman in front of you, holding aloft torches which cast lively shadows against a wall of backslashes. They are too engaged in their argument to notice you, and you can make out some of their conversation.

"No, clearly you are by the wall because when the fierce warrior comes in we both have to be able to see him," says the man.

The woman disagrees. "Impossible, I have to be here, in the

middle of the clearing. If we both stand together like this and something falls on us then we don't stand a chance."

"Look," he replies. "I'll show you."

And at that moment, you step into the pool of dancing light. They both fall silent and look at you in surprise.

To talk to them, turn to page 136.

To fight them, turn to page 221.

THE CHANCE FOR A NEW ECONOMY

The world slowly struggles back onto its feet, but it's a different world with a different law. The human population has been cut to a fraction and nature has sequestered large swathes of abandoned metropolis. Wolverhampton is patrolled by actual wolves and actual hamsters, and pigeons have reappropriated Trafalgar Square. Without skilled personnel to supervise them, Christmas tree farms across the country are quickly stripped by flocks of robins, and, lacking the necessary cull afforded by fast-moving windscreens on motorways, Britain's indigenous insects triple in size in a matter of weeks.

Once the few surviving humans have overcome the shock of losing everything they worked for all their lives, they find much to rejoice about on this beautiful lush planet where anyone can do and have whatever they want. And yet deep down everyone bears the truth in their conscience: if this experience has taught mankind anything, it's that we shouldn't in fact be allowed to have whatever we want. Unless the thing that we want is the desire to not want anything, in which case we should be allowed to want that and to want to want it. In this topsy-turvy future, man is an endangered species, and there soon becomes so much plenty that plenty itself is worthless.

Thus a unique society develops where the value of objects dictates inflation directly, and prestige is equated with a lack of valuable possessions. Britain's poorest now sleep on sheets threaded with gold and eat caviar for breakfast. The wealthiest struggle with sodden cardboard boxes under bridges, by night warming their fingertips over burning barrels of oil, by day sitting in doorways desperately trying to palm off the last of their riches to passers-by. Although comic lore advises against using all the money to buy lottery tickets, the loaded poor continue to do so in the belief that it's an effective, yet exciting, way of wasting their cash. Despite their prayers for another rollover week, some unlucky souls will of course always win yet more riches, exacerbating their wretched state.

Yes, the gap between rich and poor is both greater and more peculiar than it's ever been. It's clear to all that a fair and efficient economic system must be installed, and fast. You are elected to take hold of the situation, and after a long sleepless night thinking things over and gambling on the internet, you decide to seize and direct the mood of the day, take complete control of the situation, and see what the Swiss Army Life suggests you do.

Turn to page 80.

LET THE WRONG ONE IN

You nod.

"Yes? Yes I can? Jesus!" Ariel rolls her bloodshot eyes. "That shit is basic."

And in she comes.

THE END

IT'S A ROYAL KNOCKOUT

Removing the Royals is a difficult problem; their bunker under Buckingham Palace is heavily reinforced and they won't come out of their own accord unless you can identify and exploit their weaknesses. You search the library archives. Finding an old newspaper that predates the apocalypse, you have to smile at how different things were back in the days before we all lived in a polluted environment with a precarious economy and a terrible public transport infrastructure. But as you scan the 'Notes and Queries' page of one broadsheet, something catches your eye. There, underneath "What are the spiritual responsibilities of the Fairy Godmother?" and before "Is the phrase 'political correctness gone mad' offensive to people with real mental illness?" a reader has submitted the question:

It is well known that the Queen Mother was the first member of the Royal Family to die. What happened to the rest of them?

The response printed below is intriguing.

It is indeed an interesting question and although there are a number of rumours about this, the truth is perhaps even more surprising than fiction. This is yet another mystery that can be traced back to the mad French monarch Louis XIV. Nicknamed 'The Sun King' for his enormous size, Louis's notorious extravagance reached its astonishing peak one day in 1658 when, according to anecdote, the king rushed to the top of the Eiffel Tower and declared he'd managed to buy immortality before leaping 320 feet to certain life.

Thus invigorated, Louis swam to England where he promptly murdered the English King, George II, dressed up as him and impregnated his wife, in the process accidentally guaranteeing immortality for the English royal family. To this day, the only person capable of killing a Royal is another Royal. British Royals have traditionally declared themselves dead at an appropriate age, before disguising themselves as peasants and travelling in secret to the Isle of Wight, where the pace of life is that much slower.

The Queen Mother's supposed death at the age of 101 was probably a publicity stunt to draw attention back to the Royal Family. The funeral was certainly an impressive show, but these things should be taken with a pinch of salt.

It appears that Britain's Royal Family – almost uniquely in Europe – is comprised of immortals, and so, with treason a scientific impossibility, you are forced to come up with an alternative plan to remove the monarchy. You begin by intercepting their supply convoys, effectively starving them while you hide on the outskirts of their grounds. It's a sacrifice, for sure, but as you lie in wait in the shadows of Buckingham Palace, tucking into endless rich cakes and sublime cucumber sandwiches in your marquee, you decide it's one you're okay with on the condition that the needs of the many are being defended.

It takes a few weeks for the indestructible family to give themselves up. You're watching from your tent as the white flag is hoisted over the building and the Royals file out with their hands in the air (and in various states of undress, although this is never explained). But they're not getting away that easily. A disenchanted Britain still blames the Queen for not responding quickly enough to the public mood after Diana's death, and when rumours begin to spread that the Royals are not completely immortal, but can be killed by their own kind, the nation seizes the opportunity for payback.

Turn to page 57.

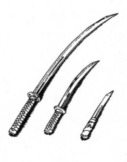

THE HOLIDAYS

It's not so much that you don't like her – you do. She's fine. But after some weeks of time travel adventures you begin to feel a bit guilty about the way she worships the ground you walk on. Andi? seems to devote all her time to trying to impress you, whisking you off to amazing alternative futures. As a time travel agent she can only show you the touristy stuff, but it's okay, you still pick up some interesting souvenirs and a flavour of local life.

You've always believed in the idea that technically there's only one road, so you are thrilled to visit a future where transport has been optimised to provide just one incredibly long train, and people get on and off at different points of its 300-mile-long carriage according to where they need to stop. There's a literal future, too, where public phones can only be used to make public phone calls, which are then broadcast over a loudspeaker to everyone in the world. There are alternate post-fossil fuel dystopias where the wi-fi is free but the electricity costs £5 a minute. There's one where God finally owns up to inventing the television, and another where culture has become so youth-orientated that people aspire to looking and behaving like children and anyone will do anything for you in exchange for a pathetically small amount of pocket money. In many cases it doesn't even have to be real money. You travel on aeroplanes where the cabin's been adjusted for peer as well as air pressure, and visit far-off lands where speed-crazed foreign taxi drivers observe a mile/km exchange rate of about 1/50 in favour of the strong mile.

But one hot midsummer afternoon, as you stand under the banners at the 2016 'PIN Pride' march, you finally realise you're not being fair to Andi? – or at any rate have got all you're going to out of the affair – and that the time has come to put an end to the relationship.

"Isn't it wonderful?" Her face is shining. "A future where people are no longer ashamed of their PIN. An environment of true trust and acceptance where we can all come out in the open about our personal account details. Don't you feel so free? 1398! 1398!"

"I don't think this is working out," you say, lowering your 'Proud To Be 9024' sign and looking at her.

"Pardon?" And you realise you said it half in your head and repeat it, louder. Andi? doesn't react, except to say, "Ah" and then "Interesting." And you think you feel a sudden chill in the air when she takes you to one side and suggests you do the next part of the journey alone.

"My time travel device is broken," you say, holding up the shattered phone.

"Don't worry," she says. "I can help. There's a method of travel called statistical acceleration. I've never tried it myself but I think you should. I really think you should." It turns out to be less optional than she suggests.

She takes both your hands in hers. "Close your eyes." After barely a moment's consideration you reply: "No."

But it doesn't make any difference.

"Statistical Accelerator," she says, brandishing a bright red 20-sided die. She sets it spinning on a fingertip. "It's like rolling a die. Except more so."

Turn to page 134.

THE BIT ABOUT THE ENTROPY PHONE

The Entropy device really does look like a phone, to the extent that even phones look like phones these days. But the head explains that it actually houses a ring laser. The beam, he says, enters a square chamber through a semi-transparent mirror, a bit like those ones they used to use to catch vain people in supermarkets. It is reflected by each corner of the square until it reaches the original mirror, where it's bounced back to the other mirrors and so on, creating a constant gyroscopic loop of light.

Interestingly, the laser ring produces a gravitational field in a similar pattern to that of water swirling down a plughole, suggesting enticing commercial possibilities for some kind of 'time travel shower' system, if not a whole bathroom. He explains the machine works via a combination of sophisticated electromagnetic technology, memory and speculation.

"You're probably wondering if it's a new technology," says the face. "Well, that depends on what you mean by new. But it's hard to put an exact age on it because, of course, it doesn't originate on Earth." You gasp, but the head remains inscrutable. "Come on, do you really think the moon causes the tides?" For the first time, you can feel eyes twinkling behind the screen. "I can't believe anyone ever buys that! It's miles away! And how do you think predictive text works? That stuff can't be explained by our Earth science alone."

And with that, the video stops abruptly and the screen reverts to the message from VICTIM. Turn to page 170.

FIGHT THE GUY, INSURED

Just to be on the safe side, you agree to buy the most expensive insurance package on his recommendation. The salesman explains that the price covers damage and loss to parts of your person and your subsequent inability to work due to injury, apathy or death.* It seems an exceptionally good deal; for just a few pounds a year you're covered for every eventuality, and apparently making a contribution towards a charity that rehouses street fundraisers.

But you're still spoiling for a fight, so, while he's busy putting away his card reader, you throw a punch at his shoulder. Somehow you miss, and when he looks up in surprise, your embarrassment overwhelms your manly urge to wrestle with a stranger, and you drop to the floor and pretend to be doing up a shoelace. While you're down there you notice your laces do actually need to be done up, and by the time you're finished the Life Insurance Guy is handing you some paperwork to sign.

"The thing is, death doesn't have to be a killer," he says, and his eyes lose focus in their efforts to track increasingly cider-washed thoughts. "I used to be an actor, you know; it's not so different. I believe life should be like a wonderful play. Enjoyable, well-directed, meaningful –" A melancholy pause.

---

* You are something of a physical wreck and the truth is some kind of life insurance is probably well overdue. Your obsessive-compulsive behaviours and high intolerance of disorder culminate in a tendency to become so anxious in social situations that you often lose all control of your muscles and simply spasm helplessly several feet into the air.

"It's the intervals I have trouble with."

"Which intervals?" You're confused.

"All of them," he says sadly. "With their opportunities for the audience to escape. But particularly the interval between birth and death. For the punter it's the best part: the part that's all about you. The part where you get to choose whether to sit quietly or get up and do some queuing. But it's over far too soon."

Apparently seeing you as something of kindred spirit, the insurance salesman throws a meaty arm round your shoulder and launches into his life story. Years ago, he says, he'd been earmarked for greatness. He had been a prodigious and troubled actor, and exorcised his many demons through a number of one-man plays in which he played thinly-veiled versions of the people causing him the most problems in his life, all coming to harm in a variety of imaginative ways. But honesty comes at a price, and within a year of taking to the stage as a self-styled serial monologist he found himself rejected by his friends, ostracised by his family and cruelly mocked by caricaturists hired by any number of ex-girlfriends.

Things were bad. He tells you how he lost a lot of money on cars, women and online alcoholism before declaring moral bankruptcy and going into TV. You try to look sympathetic*. His career in media production was destined to be short-lived too, however, and all his major gambles flopped. The insurance salesmen's voice is leaden with regret as he tells you how he

---

* Though your intellectual brilliance is not in doubt, most other areas of your life have been seriously retarded by a lack of 'people skills'. You've always struggled to gauge tone and mood from expressions and indeed recognise your own mother's face in a line-up of one.

attempted to finally fill a perceived gap between serious 'issue' documentaries and lighthearted shows for younger viewers with the suicide gameshow *Bring On the Victim Outline* in which contestants leapt from tall buildings and in the seconds before impact tried to arrange themselves into the chalk body shapes drawn on the pavement below. Equally unsuccessful was the worthy-but-fun two-parter *Famine Victims* and *Famine Victims A Year On: have they kept the weight off?*.

Thus, in his fourth decade, he abandoned the media in favour of a career as a life-insurance salesman, specialising in accidental, premature and suspicious deaths and keeping the flames fanned in an industry hell-bent on exploiting people's fear of unlikely tragedy.

"To be honest, I didn't know what was going on in my life back then," he slurs. "I didn't know if I was washing up a knife or just serrating a scrubbing brush, if you catch my drift." You do. But it takes a moment.

"And that was when I had the epiphany!" That smile again – and something of the showbiz sparkle returns to his eyes. "If people could be safeguarded from the worst, we would never have to pay out at all. Which is why," he gets up as if to leave, "your Life Protection will shield you from 99% of global genocides! You can trust this product to keep you safe, because if you think about it, it's in our interest that nothing bad happens to you. Like how it never rains when you take an umbrella with you."

"R-r-really?"*

---

* Your slight stammer has always been a barrier to making friends, except friends who also suffer from speech impediments, of whom you have a

"Yes. It is based on the same science as...umbrellas. Anyway, thanks for buying Life Protection!" He begins to walk away as quickly as his intoxicated legs will carry him, shooting a quick look back over his shoulder. "Don't forget! Life Protection guarantees immortality!"

"HUH? What the –?!"

"Can't hear you! Sorry! Give me a call sometime. No hurry, ha ha!" And he's gone, no doubt off to find another funeral to hang around in the hope of picking up some business from another unsuspecting mourner.

You look at the card, but so far as you can tell, there are no contact details on it, and when you go to call him back, he's gone. There's a sudden creaking sound – in the entrance of a nearby shop, an automatic door is swinging slowly open of its own accord.

Turn to page 77.

Turn to page 77.

surprisingly large number. And while others may be baffled by your intense distrust of "bad" typefaces, colours and numbers and catalogue of compulsions (literally, you like to keep a record), they are all completely logical to you, and become more pronounced with stress.

GO BACK TO SLEEP

You are, understandably, exhausted. There's a suitable bench in a park nearby and you bundle up your rucksack to form a makeshift pillow and pull your emergency waterproof jacket around you as far as it will go. You're so tired, in fact, that even the cold metallic bench against your skin can't stop your eyelids dropping and your muscles softening. Within seconds you begin to drift off, and in that space between wakefulness and true sleep you have a dream about a very strange library.

The upper shelves are piled with paperbacks, while thin, ragged hardbacks are packed in busily underneath. Suspecting you might be here for a while, you pull one out at random and turn it over in your hands. It's called *The Long History of Time*. You put it back quickly and pick another. It's a self-help book called *How I Stopped Worrying And Learned To Love The Heat Death Of The Universe*. You file it roughly where you found it, and go again. The next one's rather severe-looking, an impression largely down to the thin, spiky font chosen for the cover, but not helped by the unusual title: *What's the Time?* it says. Then, answering its own question, *No o'clock. Time doesn't exist.* This book is a perfect cube, with writing down the sides and spine as well as on the pages, and the text on the cover alone suggests its thesis is a redefinition of eternity. *What if eternity is everything happening together, simultaneously? What if the 'arrow of time'*, the text printed on the ends of the pages asks, *is nothing but an elaborate illusion of consciousness?* Interesting. Hoping it won't all be written in rhetorical questions, you fall back into a saggy chair and begin.

It's a struggle to get your head round it all initially, particularly as the narrative seems to jump around all over the place, and you find yourself flicking backwards and forwards in the book, keeping thumbs and fingers in the pages as you forget what you've read, what you're reading, what you're going to read. Soon you're immersed in it, allowing yourself to be carried away by somebody's incredibly challenging vision of reality, a reality which bears no resemblance to anything you've been taught about physics or maths or, most importantly of course, Euclidean geometry. As you fall deeper under the book's spell, fragments of ideas swim to the surface of your awareness and disperse. There's a vague hint of a sense of an inkling that every possible thing hangs in space simultaneously, along with an intuition that motion isn't what we think it is. Or thought it was. You feel all these things faintly, as a hazy synaesthesia of taste and colour. Mainly, though, you just feel a quite amazing stillness – the stillness that only a complete absence of time can bring about. Your body is all at once tight and restful and strange, your limbs pressed up against the air, moulding it with each microscopic movement. Deeper and deeper. It's like the sleep of unconsciousness, so much so that you may in fact be falling asleep. But after a while – difficult to say how long for many reasons – you emerge from your trance with a sense of certainty that you've consumed all the information in the book despite failing to quite remember any of it. With no understanding of what's just happened, you're back on the very first page.

When you've finished, or started, or whatever, you grab another, this time from the bottom. They're kids' books, and you've selected a slim but colourfully illustrated volume entitled

Goldilocks and the three exoplanets, only one of which might speculatively be hospitable for the life. You put it back and pull out a nursery rhyme anthology. 'Humpty Entropy' makes for interesting reading – they couldn't put him back together again without thoroughly challenging the second law of thermodynamics. The mouse in their 'Hickory Dickory Dock' ran up the clock at the speed of light and, upon running down again, discovered less time had passed for him than for his mousie friends, who were now all old and bent, with little grey whiskers. Meanwhile, the young hero of this version of 'Rock-a-bye Baby' falls out of a Newton's cradle (unsurprisingly, since the desk toy was never designed to support infants) and hits the ground actually quite hard because gravity is acting on it with a force of approximately 40N. And needless to say, the new interpretation of Doctor Foster does little to relieve your doubts about whether the eponymous character is indeed medically qualified. It's all entertaining enough as a temporary distraction, but you can't help wondering whether someone's trying to tell you something. Is time not what you thought it was? Can you circumvent a nuclear disaster simply by looking at entropy from the other side?

Whatever that weird book thinks, you feel certain that time will always be there under your feet, flowing along like the irrepressible river of moments it is, while the cycle of life goes round and round again. But what if it wasn't? Would it make any difference? It's not like you can do anything about it anyway. You're just one guy. One guy with two pairs of pants on. Whether it's one damn thing after another, or all the damn things at the same time, you decide that after everything you've been through today, eternity is starting to look quite attractive. Although, of course, you'll never overcome the age difference.

And then you drop into a whole new level of sleep. A peace-smoothed unbroken bath of a sleep. Such a deep sleep, in fact, that you don't even wake up when the bomb goes off.

THE END

FIGHT THEM

You pick up a six-foot polystyrene tilde and start running at them, screaming "I never did understand what these were for!" before tripping over a rogue full stop and falling hard on your face. The pair watch in silence as you pick yourself up and discreetly check your nose isn't bleeding. After a very long silence the woman turns to the man.

"Oh no," she frowns and shakes her head. "That's not how I imagined it at all."

The man looks alarmed. "No, he's not with me! But he does seem...hostile."

They both collapse with laughter at this, although as you sit on the floor rubbing your grazed arm and twitching anxiously, you're not sure why. Nevertheless, you're relieved to have inadvertently ended the quarrel, and decide that it's probably a good time to strike. With words this time.

Turn to page 136.

FINDING SURVIVORS

A quick search of the area reveals several discrete groups of survivors. Recreational cannibals have considerable staying power it turns out, as do fans of medieval reenactment, who are able to make mead and generate their own folksy entertainment. Young males so absorbed in orchestrating tabletop battles in Warhammer shops that they're genuinely oblivious to any real war raging outside also seem to have pulled through, although they have yet to notice anything's changed and perhaps never will. A disproportionate number of craft hobbyists seem to make it too, perhaps due to their superior resourcefulness and the additional structural reinforcement afforded to their homes by their reluctance to throw anything away. Also granted an unexpected reprieve are the residents of high security prisons, the Amish, and those in the middle of robbing bank vaults[*]. Meanwhile, back in London, a few wealthy, sheltered apocosceptics acknowledge no change in their situation and continue to try to run their lifeless kids to the school gates and back in unnecessarily large vehicles until long after fossil fuels have run out and everyone is dead, including them.

Turn to page 29.

---

[*] Apocalyptic myth warns us of dangerous biker gangs, but it doesn't take much thought to realise the group of survivors posing the greatest threat to peace are in fact the Amish ex-cons. And yet they continue to walk freely among us.

HELP YOUR PARENTS IN THEIR EVIL PLAN TO MAKE YOU LIVE WITH THEM FOREVER AND DESTROY THE WORLD

Clearly you weren't going to get out of there alive, and you agree to work with the evil duo in the secret hope that it might be possible to use your situation for good. There are, you suppose, a few people here who didn't deserve to be abducted and killed, and you feel morally obliged to at least try to revive them and return them to their own time. Your parents leave you in the bedroom they've had built especially for you and say they're "heading up to bed" and that you shouldn't "stay up too late".

That night you have a terrible dream. It's cold. Very cold. It's fair to say you've never been so cold. You try to move, but you can't. Close to your face there's a concave panel of clear hard material, and at eye level, on the reverse, some engraved lettering. SCINOYRC. You guess it says cryonics, in Polish perhaps, and with a gasp and a start, you wake to find yourself in an upright position and see the blanket's on the floor.

Although you were loath to tell your parents, the truth is you've never really believed in the idea of cryosuspension. It all feels so arbitrary somehow. If people are going to gamble their earnings against a distant future possibility, why stop with resuscitation? Why not bet your life savings against the chance you might one day become the multimillionaire inventor of Massively Multiplayer Football before fathering the first baby in space and becoming Supreme God of Everything? Actually, why not? Stranger things could happen. If you start paying towards resurrection in your early twenties, the only thing anyone can be sure of is that you're selling decades of life in exchange for centuries of death. But if you have yourself frozen while you're still alive, there is so much life you may never know, so many questions you may never get answers to. What is a 'second cousin' anyway? What's the definition of smart-casual? Will they ever make a remote control that goes 'Pyow!'?

And yet, the idea frightens and fascinates you in equal measure. You might wake as a vegetable, the membranes in your head burst like berries – or worse, with the feeling of antifreeze creeping through your capillaries as you undergo an emergency blood transfusion with an internal combustion engine. You might rise to find you're in the middle of a war or a world of superevolved alien-human hybrids whose thoughts and feelings can be communicated only in voiceover. Yes, there's a chance the world would be better, but you certainly wouldn't come back rich, surrounded by anyone you know, or any less stupid than you were when you first picked up the Frozen Assets card and bought yourself eternal life. Still, it's interesting. You can't deny that.

You notice your parents have left a brochure hopefully next to your bed. The title is 'Madame Tussaud's Cryonics' with the caption 'Because everyone's a special individual particle of liquid nitrogen'. There is a picture of a snowflake on it.

To read the brochure, turn to page 89.
To explore on foot, turn to page 101.

OFF THE RAILS

The publication is called 'Off The Rails' and has the strapline 'Getting you from A to A'. You let it fall open on a random page – some kind of column geared towards commuters. The piece seems to be about coping online in this future, without falling into one of the many pitfalls of circular logic in an apparently paradox-heavy world.

"Things have changed for all of us in recent years," it begins. "There are more and more places in this world that we simply cannot visit. Philosophically abject zones. Spaces of otherness that human eyes should never be allowed to directly encounter. The interiors of our own bodies, for example. Bins without bags in. The insides of office kettles. And although I know it's difficult to believe, there's a case to be made that the internet is behind this self-referential minefield in which we must now struggle to exist. Each delight and danger has its correspondent on the outside, and just like the real world, the web is pitted with unpleasantness." You glance around nervously. Your double is still looking at his phone.

"There are many unwritten rules and paradoxes in internet land. The first unwritten rule is also the first paradox: that one must never write down the rules. Another states in clear invisibility that we should avoid looking back at our old websites for the same reason that we shouldn't become preoccupied with revisiting past homes, schools and loves. Tempting as it is to while away the hours scrolling through source code, sighing 'I remember when all this was form fields', we really must resist. Because nostalgia is always going to end in disappointment, either with the past or with the present. It's a question of self-preservation. No one would argue, really, with the fact that the internet used to be better. Much better. But going back to the websites of your youth, you'll find it all seems smaller – then you'll become embarrassed and laugh at the thought, realising it's just you that has grown. We must never look back, and we must certainly never peer directly into the dark and powerful paradoxes of the web."

Turn to page 156.

CHECK YOUR PHONE

You pull out your laptop and find a faint wireless signal. Selecting one of the internet's equally popular search engines at random, you do a quick bit of research. Somehow, perhaps due to the phone's insistence on upgrading itself, you've lost several years overnight. And in the intervening time the political situation has gone from ridiculous to precarious to ridiculously precarious. It seems the explosion you'd heard down the phone took place on a Postcode territorial boundary, and now each side blames the other for breaching the ceasefire.

So it's the year 2012, and London is on the brink of a devastating atomic event. It seems things became dangerous around 2011, when a neighbourhood feud between two competing postmen was allowed to get out of hand. The explosion you created resulted in the death of the band Franz Ferdinand, who happened to be passing at the worst possible moment. Since the band were aligned with The Postal Service, who were in turn established supporters of the Occupiers, a whole chain of alliances fell like dominoes within weeks.

With no one taking responsibility for the explosion and no confirmation it was an accident, rumours quickly spiralled out of control. Lines of blame crisscrossed the globe, with the East accusing the West of being morally unconscionable, the *Daily Mail* blaming working mothers, and everyone else blaming the grey squirrels. There were attempts at reconciliation to start with, faint flickers of optimism. Perhaps no one was to blame – maybe the sudden catastrophic descent into global thermonuclear war just 'one of those things'? Or a symptom of a greater international malaise? But the meetings never ended well, because after the rich countries had finished looking suspiciously at the poor ones, and the poor ones had finished emptying their pockets and doing the sad eyes, both went home and secretly drew up designs for nuclear warheads. Without the Games Master to look after his characters and control imaginative play, the universe has been driven to the brink of chaos. To top it all, the Olympic plans are no longer on track, partly because of the impending Armageddon, partly because the track still hasn't been built.

Turn to page 63.

CHECKING YOUR EMAIL

You open your inbox, asking the public computer to try its best not to 'remember' your password, and note with interest that the spammer work ethic can't be dampened by the imminent apocalypse. You have a few messages selling Repl1ca Watches, a product, you assume, aimed at accuracy-obsessed props departments, and there at the bottom of thirty emails offering to sell you a 'duplicate spam blocker' you find a message from an address you only vaguely recognise.

You are receiving this update because you once signed up for newsletters from 'The Sky Is Falling: Knee-jerk News From The Knife-Edge of Paranoia'. Well, now the sky really is falling. Please disregard previous emails to similar effect: this time we mean it. The end has come and we are all going to die. And then come back to life and eat people's brains, while still being dead, somehow. We're a bit shady on the science to be honest, but we promise: it is actually happening this time. Still, if you are reading this it probably means there are survivors, so there is at least some hope. Unless you are dead or a ghost. If you are not dead or a ghost we advise getting

off your computer and finding somewhere safer
to hide from dead people and ghosts. Like
I say, I know I said it before but I do
actually mean it this time, really. Forget
all those other times, they were mistakes but
this definitely isn't. No way.

At this point the message descends into even more delirious
gibberish before the infected emailer seems to get it together to
hit 'Send'. The next message says,

NO IGNORE THAT STAY WHERE YOU ARE I CHANGED MY
MIND ACTUALLY FOR SOME REASON. PS BRAINS.

Turn to page 184.

TALK TO THE LIFE INSURANCE SALESMAN

"I'm sorry for your loss," the suit man says as you approach. He's holding up a black object you recognise as your wallet. "I assume this is yours." One hand flies to your back pocket and you snatch the wallet back off him with the other.

"I thought you meant the loss of the Games Master," you say.

"Oh yes! I'm quite sorry about that as well. I hope you're not feeling your mortality too keenly at the moment." What an odd thing to say, you think. But, as he smiles a slightly strange little smile and lays a hand on your shoulder, you realise that is exactly what you're feeling. "You know what you could use right now?"

"A drink?" There's a note of hope in your voice. The man in the suit laughs a hearty, practiced gameshow host laugh.

"Well, yes. Yes, a drink. Not what I was going to say, but an excellent idea." You can't find a pub but manage to pick up some budget own-brand cider and, since it's a nice day, sit and drink it outside the church. Near some bins.

"You know," he crumples his fifth can and tosses it into the churchyard, narrowly missing a widow. "There's a way of feeling better about your inedible – ineffable – indelible – certain death. After all, it might come sooner than you think!" He gestures extravagantly as he delivers the line and you're not sure if you've received a threat against your life or won a holiday in Granada. Maybe you have won a holiday, but it's a really bad one where you're staying on a building site, like on *Holidays from Hell*. And while you're studying his face slightly fearfully, trying to work out if he knows something you don't and what the Spanish for 'cockroaches in the en suite' is, the man in the suit thrusts a business card under your nose. You're just about to take it when he changes his mind and hands you a different one.

"FROZEN ASSETS INSURANCE" announces the glossy foil print, and underneath "LAUGHING IN THE FACE OF YOUR FAMILY'S BEREAVEMENT". You look up from the card and are almost blinded by the opportunistic life insurance salesman's broad icy grin. In a way, it's all a little disappointing. You don't have many friends and had been feeling hopeful about your new drinking pal, but as ever logic prevails[*] and you weigh up the offer.

"Well I am about to go on a dangerous journey," you muse, the alcohol amplifying your voice to a deafening volume. "Can you give me some more information?"

"Nnnnng sorry!" The salesman's shoulders tense in theatrical regret. "But I can tell you this is no ordinary life insurance. In the event of injury, we will pay out a lot, and in the event of death…well, there'll be millions on the way to your next of kin." He pulls out a small tape recorder. "Do you mind if I record our conversation? For training purposes?"

"Erm…"

---

[*] In many ways you possess an extraordinary brain, solving the trickiest Sudoku in your head and analysing the science of *Star Trek* in more detail even than the writers, as they admitted themselves in their replies to your letters. But these qualities haven't always been conducive to making friends; if anything the opposite is true!

"Great! Thank you." He leans in close and his breath smells like rancid apples. "The truth is, it's not for training purposes. I collect sounds. Mainly screams for personal use."

And struck with fear and an awareness of your status as warrior-author of the Fantasy Universe, you are quite suddenly overcome by the need to have a fight. This guy might just be in the wrong place at the wrong time.

To fight the guy, turn to page 144.

To buy life insurance from him, then fight him, turn to page 213.

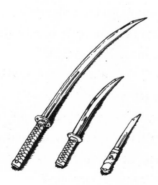

THE ACTUAL END

And so it is that you toil away alone for millennia in the cryolabs beneath the nightmarish spires of Standard Deviation Mountain, deeply absorbed in your work and oblivious to the goings-on above the surface. The wax eruption never happens but the human race eventually wipes itself out anyway in a centuries-long battle with extraterrestrials who landed on Earth with goodwill and gifts but consistently parked their crafts in spaces that weren't allocated to them. All those residents subsidising the aliens through their own ground rent were understandably irritated and, with the grim attitude of 'If I can't have the space, no one can', filled in their parking spaces with 20-tonne concrete blocks. It was this bloody-mindedness that led to humankind becoming embroiled in an interplanetary battle it had no hope of winning and which it had failed to anticipate despite decades of accumulative warnings issued by the aliens through regular horoscopes. Having successfully extinguished the population, the aliens looted Earth for its most precious artifacts and returned to their home planet to hold an exhibition of mankind's greatest sculptures and paintings displayed all upside down and back to front.

Throughout the drama you remain underground, quite oblivious, and all alone for hundreds of thousands of years. With time you come to quite enjoy the company of the cryo-bodies, talking to them, sharing problems and memories, reading them stories. It's amazing how concentrating focuses the mind, and one day you hit upon a solution, an ingenious way of reactivating the human body without damaging its delicate tissues. Not only that, but you create a perpetual motion machine based on your own DNA which is capable of freezing bodies indefinitely, or at least until the sun goes supernova.[*]

The revival formula on a piece of paper in your hand, you stand in front of the legion corpses, and realise this is the moment. The time you've been waiting for, for so long. So why don't you feel more excited? Surely the idea of liberating these abductees from their icy prisons has been what's kept you going all these years? But there's no joy in your heart. You think of them creaking back into life, running outside and back in again and treading mud through your pristine lair. You think of the noise they might make, the questions they will ask, the demands they'll make on your routine. You think of the time you'll have to spend educating them about how to live in this future; you know from experience that it can take days just to teach one person something as simple as the correct way to load the dishwasher.

And you find you just can't do it. Everything is in order now. As far as you're concerned, chaos is a thing of the distant past. It seems that, ultimately, you'd rather be solitary, forever alone and a little insane, than have to share your stuff with someone else.

One day, when you're very very old and you've watched all your DVDs a million times and edited all the scenes from

---

[*] Over the millennia you spend alone, you become increasingly irritated that although all the other celestial bodies have names, those most closely associated with Earth are still known only as 'Sun' and 'Moon'. Since you are, properly, finally, absolutely the last human alive now, you decide to rename them. You ponder for hundreds of years but can't think of anything good, so you take to calling them Whitey and Yellowy.

Memento and *Lost* into chronological order, you accept that you are finally bored of life. Perhaps too bored to go on. And quite by chance you notice there's one empty casket left and pause in front of it for a moment. You are the only one in the world who knows how to revive bodies from cryostasis; without you these people don't stand a chance of waking up. Of all the decisions you've had to make since you began this incredible quest, this is the single most important one. It's no longer just about having a fight, using a device, or saving one person's life: this is serious. The choice you make now will affect the future survival of the human race.

Sod it, you think. What they won't know can't hurt them. Without a moment's further thought you step inside, slide the door closed and hook up the drip to your wrist.

And then, finally, you sleep.

THE ACTUAL END

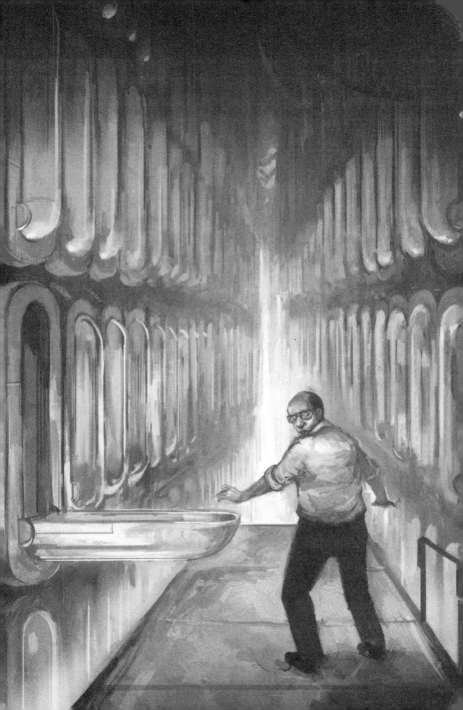

ACKNOWLEDGMENTS

I wouldn't say this was the easiest thing I've ever done, but it was certainly the hardest. I guess that's always the way with autobiography.

So thanks are due to all my friends for not minding when I disappeared to write a book and emerged with this nonsense. More specifically, thanks must go to Tom, who not only read the thing again and again until it made him physically sick and didn't stop even when the doctors begged him to, but then went on to deal with the technical side of things. Thanks too to James Wallis, both for holding onto his D&D books and for the brilliant advice that I was able to forget very effectively. My appreciations to Tom Sharp and the amazing Stone Soup, to Jon Hodgson for the beautiful illustration at the end, and to Helen Zaltzman for her truly exceptional pedantry. Humble indebtedness to David Schneider, Polly Vernon and David Quantick for the accolades and support, and affectionate gratitude to my foolhardy enablers Snowbooks for letting me do this at all. But most of all my thanks to thank you, nerd, both for inspiring this book and for accepting the challenge of riding out the chaos that is my head.

With apologies to fans of *Watchmen*, *Star Trek* and *House,* employees and relatives of Madame Tussauds, the Royal Family, Les Dennis, Gok Wan, Demi Moore, Noah Hathaway, Amish ex-cons, Viewdata, the Post Office and the Royal Mail, Zork, all coffee shops, memory champions, charity volunteers, gamers, geeks, supernatural beings, superheroes and supervillains everywhere. I was only joking.

Leila Johnston, September 2009